PRAISE FOR ARNOLD ZABLE AND
CAFE SCHEHERAZADE

'Zable has worked that miracle of storytelling
which puts our hearts in our mouths even when we
know that it will all come right in the end.'
Judith Armstrong, *Australian Book Review*

'He explores the shadow side of Australian multiculturalism—
the immigrant and minority experiences of traumatic loss
and displacement...a celebration of the immigrants' resilience
and creativity. In Zable's eloquent style, storytelling is
heightened by pathos, tragedy and lyricism...In his journalism,
Arnold Zable is distinguished by his empathy for minorities
and human rights. In his longer works a strain of romantic
yearning finds expression in lyrical landscapes and in reverence
for the capacity of the human spirit.'
Felicity Bloch, *Age*

'It is the sense of wonder, not the repetition of horror, that
distinguishes Zable's Holocaust stories and makes him one of
the best tellers of his kind. *Cafe Scheherazade*...transcends the
distinction between fiction and non-fiction.'
Ivor Indyk, *Sydney Morning Herald*

'Zable conjures the extraordinary from within the
seemingly ordinary and plain fact takes on the lustre
of poetry...Alternately moving and joyful, this book
celebrates the tenaciousness of the human spirit.'
William Gourlay, *Australian Way*

'This is truly a man who believes in the power of stories.'
Martin Flanagan, *Age*

Arnold Zable is a widely published writer, storyteller
and educator. Formerly a lecturer at Melbourne University,
he has worked in a variety of jobs in the USA, India,
Papua New Guinea, Europe, South-East Asia and China.
His books include *Wanderers and Dreamers*, and the
acclaimed *Jewels and Ashes*, which won five literary
awards. He is also the author of two children's books.

Zable performs as a storyteller, drawing on his experiences,
travels and knowledge of Yiddish culture. He has worked
with Aboriginal elders on educational projects. He has
conducted writing workshops in universities, schools,
community centres and with migrants and refugees.

Arnold Zable lives in Melbourne with his wife and son.

Cafe Scheherazade

Arnold Zable

TEXT PUBLISHING
MELBOURNE AUSTRALIA

The Text Publishing Company
171 La Trobe Street
Melbourne Victoria 3000
Australia

This edition published 2001, reprinted 2001 (four times), 2002

Printed and bound by Griffin Press
Designed by Chong Weng-ho
Typeset in Stempel Garamond 12/17.5 by J&M Typesetting

National Library of Australia
Cataloguing-in-Publication data:

Zable, Arnold.

Cafe Scheherazade.

ISBN 1 876485 71 X.

I. Title.

A823.3

The author has been assisted by the Commonwealth Government through the Australia Council, its arts funding and advisory body.

To Melbourne's first storytellers:
the Wurundjeri and Bunurong people.
And to all those who are still in search of a haven,
a place they can call home.

King Shahriyar, ruler of the ancient kingdom of Persia, having discovered the infidelity of his queen, resolved to have a fresh wife every night and have her beheaded at daybreak. This caused great consternation in the land. Fully aware of this grave situation, Scheherazade, the daughter of a senior court official, the grand vizier, contrived to become Shahriyar's wife. She so amused him with stories for a thousand and one nights that the king revoked his cruel decree. The courageous queen also gained the love and gratitude of her people and, to this day, audiences the world over are seduced by her tales.

~

I

In Acland Street, St Kilda, there stands a cafe called Scheherazade. As to how it came to have such a name, therein lies a story. Many stories in fact, recounted at a table in the back room where the proprietors, Mr and Mrs Zeleznikow, Avram and Masha, sit most nights of the week and eat, hold court, greet customers, check accounts, argue and reminisce. What else is there to do on this rain-sodden Melbourne night, as pedestrians rugged in overcoats stroll on pavements glistening grey, past shops laden with slices of Black Forest cake where they pause, and hesitate, before succumbing to the temptation to buy, well, just one slice. Perhaps two. What harm can it do?

This is how it is in Acland Street, an avenue of old-world dreams. This is how it is in Scheherazade, a cafe of old-world tales. And, of the countless stories which would not exhaust even a thousand and one nights in the telling, the most fascinating of all is how it came to pass, that in 1958 Avram and Masha decided to call their audacious venture Scheherazade.

For it was audacious to come in from the cold, with barely a penny to spare, to begin, in mid-life already, an entirely new enterprise, a cafe of all things, in a shop front where for many years had stood a milk bar called O'Shea's.

When Avram and Masha insisted on renaming it

Scheherazade their friends told them this would be suicide. The business would be doomed to failure from the start. Their clients would not be able to pronounce such a name, let alone be drawn towards the continental cuisine which, in time, began to grace the menu. 'Call it Masha's. Or Avram's. Or Babushka's even, if you must have an exotic name. But Scheherazade? Even we have trouble pronouncing it.'

Scheherazade it remained.

'Martin, it could not have been otherwise,' Masha tells me, as a waitress delivers the main course of chicken schnitzel and potato latkes to the proprietors' permanent table in the back room. 'This you will understand once you hear the full story.'

All the while our conversation is interrupted by a nod here, an aside there, a hasty conversation on the mobile phone, a snatch of gossip from an acquaintance dropping by, as Avram, and now Masha, turn to greet yet another long-time friend.

Slowly the story trickles out: between sips of borscht and wine, between main course and dessert, between cheese blintzes and cups of tea spiced with lemon. And again the next night, for I have to return night after winter's night to the table in the back room, graced with wallpaper boasting scenes of the Moulin Rouge, can-can girls in full flight, an appropriate background for an epic tale which encompasses a rendezvous in a Parisian nightclub, an apple brandy called Calvados, a nurse tending wounded sailors in the Black Sea port of Odessa, a band of partisans roaming the forests and swamps of Lithuania, perilous escapes over closely guarded borders, an ocean journey halfway across the globe, a young girl awakening in a city of minarets to the resonant echo of a muezzin's call...

Enough! Here at least is the short of it.

'Martin, I am sorry, there can be no short of it,' insists Avram.

'That would be impossible,' agrees Masha.

'But a journalist cannot spend so much time on one story! I have columns to write! Deadlines to meet! Assignments to complete!' I tell them when, yet again, they take me on a detour, and I will have to return the next night for more episodes in a vast tale that appears to have no end, and not even a beginning, as we move back through the centuries to an anecdote about yet another ancestor, another hazardous journey, another legendary city.

Such as Vilna. Vilnius. The Jerusalem of Lithuania, with its renowned yeshivas and houses of prayer, crumbling castles and fortress walls, elegant boulevards, cobblestone lanes, and its attics and garrets crowded with would-be sages and talmudic scholars, obsessed rebels and pamphleteers, hell-bent on changing a world that seemed to be forever spinning out of control.

It was into this city that, in 1924, Avram Zeleznikow was born, the son of revolutionaries, devout members of the Bund, the labour movement that captured the souls of countless Eastern European Jews.

'I was reared on Bund legends,' says Avram in his lilting Yiddish. Each word is carefully wrought. Each sentence has its melody, each paragraph its song. And when he glides into

English there is a continuity in syntax for this was the last of Avram's six languages. English is a language still in the forming, still straining for meaning, a language which eventually fails him as he falls back into the mother tongue to weave the tale of his revolutionary past.

He begins his story as a romance, nurtured in clandestine meetings and the prison cells of a dying empire. The heroine of this romance, Avram's mother, Etta Stock, was born in the Ukrainian town of Tulchin in 1881, the year that Tsar Alexander the Second was assassinated, a year of chaos, in which mobs rampaged through the Jewish quarters of Russian cities and towns. In the tens of thousands the inhabitants fled. In ragged bands, they stole across borders to ports scattered along the European coastline. In desperation they clambered onto ocean liners and freighters, on which they sailed to all corners of the globe to remake their lives.

And those who could not flee turned to thoughts of revolution and Red messiahs who would deliver them from lifetimes of fear. Others dreamt of the decaying walls of Jerusalem, and sought an end to an ancient exile. Still others clung to their God and houses of worship, their psalms and scriptures, their prayers and preachers, with increased fervour and zeal.

Among the faithful was Etta's father, Avram Stock: a fiddler. A klezmer musician who performed at weddings and bar mitzvahs; a minstrel who played for his supper at the celebrations of the Tulchin aristocracy; a pious Hasid who adhered to the

613 laws of his desert-wandering forebears; a man who punctuated his days according to the dictates of prescribed texts. And a perplexed father who could do nothing but frown upon the errant ways of his daughter, Etta, when she followed the siren call of a new god named revolution to the Black Sea port of Odessa, in the very first year of the new century.

This is a tale of many cities: each one consumed by the momentum of history. Each one recalled at a table in a cafe called Scheherazade, in a seaside suburb that sprawls upon the very ends of the earth, within a city that contains the traces of many cities.

Such as Odessa. The new Odessa is a stroll from Scheherazade. Masha alerts me to the fact. Compared to Avram, she is more firmly attuned to the present. She exudes an intense curiosity. It can be seen in the distinct lines that criss-cross her face. It can be deduced from her quick, deliberate steps. It can be seen in the neatly cut suits she wears. It can be sensed from her bearing, so upright and proud. It can be heard in her English, which is refined, if somewhat accented. And it can be inferred from her observations, her sharp retorts, the remarks she inserts into Avram's monologues.

Yes, the new Odessa is a mere stroll away, Masha tells me. Make your way into Acland Street. Turn left by the Indian take-away into Shakespeare Grove. Walk past the gaping mouth of the moon, patron saint of Luna Park, past the screams of revellers clinging to the evening skies as they career, at break-neck speeds, on the roller-coaster ride. Cross the car-choked

7

Esplanade to the palm trees that line the foreshore, and proceed to the beachfront, accompanied by the soothing aroma of sea breezes.

It is here that they congregate, the Russian emigres of the 1990s, the latest wave of wanderers in search of a haven from a troubled past. They lie on the soft sands of their new world, and remember old Odessa, its dockyards and palaces, its courtyards filled with washing flapping on makeshift lines, its noise-ridden workshops and cafes, and the melody of tenement children at play.

They stroll the St Kilda foreshore and pier, and recall the Odessa waterfront, its run-down eating houses, its rickety warehouses and loading ramps, its wharves and marinas, crowded with ferries that once conveyed them into the Black Sea on weekend cruises. They glance at the bay, and are reminded of the turquoise waters of their receding pasts. And when night descends they stroll to Scheherazade for a bowl of apple compote, a bite of almond torte, and recall bands performing in park rotundas, evenings at state theatres which resembled Turkish castles, and nights at the Odessa Opera where orchestras accompanied the singers of a dying empire.

And, just as nostalgia threatens to overwhelm them, they recall the one-room apartments in which they perspired on summer nights, the slow-moving queues for rationed supplies, and the sub-zero winters during which they stumbled out into damp courtyards smelling of urine and sweat, to relieve themselves in communal latrines choked with the waste of many families.

So their Odessa may not have been very different from the city in which Etta Stock arrived in the year 1900. Tartars strolled in black fezzes alongside Turks in tight-bound turbans. Jews en route to the Holy Land and Muslims on their once in a lifetime pilgrimage to Mecca prayed in its synagogues and mosques. Gypsies and troubadours performed in its wine cellars and bars. From its boulevards ships could be seen emerging from the fog, bearing merchandise from distant lands; while at night, drunken sailors, mumbling in disparate tongues, stalked the alleys in search of brothels and gaming dens, and conspirators gathered in concealed meeting places to plot the overthrow of the Tsar.

In Odessa, Etta studied nursing. To pay for her studies she worked in a factory where she was drawn into a cell of the Russian socialist movement. She became obsessed with saving the world. She marched in demonstrations under the cold gaze of gendarmes. She distributed illicit pamphlets and newspapers, and travelled to neighbouring villages on covert missions. She sat on committees that argued over strategy until the dawn light sponged the skies. And she worked in an underground printing press in the city of Kishinev alongside the young Joseph Stalin.

At least, this is what Avram claims. It is a family legend which he loves to recount, one of the many anecdotes which inflate his pride.

'You see? My family is part of history!' he exclaims. 'You see? My mother was a rebel, a daring fighter, a woman of the world!'

Another night has flown. The neon sign over the entrance blinks Scheherazade in rounds of lilac, blue and rose. Proprietors are drawing the shutters over their stores. The last customers are stumbling out through Scheherazade's doors.

'Martin, I warned you,' says Masha. 'This is a story without end.'

But by now I am entranced. I may have been drawn here as a journalist in search of an intriguing tale, but this is far greater than a column, a life story at a glance. There are moments when I no longer know where I am. Time extends beyond time and I return the next night as if lured by a recurring dream.

Scheherazade is crowded with theatregoers and lonely men sipping tea. Two powdered streetwalkers eat toasted cheese on rye. A medical student reads *Gray's Anatomy* over a bowl of chicken soup. Waitresses run from the kitchen balancing trays laden with steaming meals.

So take your time. Sit down at our table. Break bread. Share our bottle of red. Observe the white-haired storyteller Avram, his hands in motion, his voice straining to maintain its vigour, his ample eyebrows darting up and down as he proclaims that the century truly began in 1905, with frenzied young men and women careering through the streets of Tsarist Russia screaming: *'Daloi Nikolai! Daloi Nikolai!* Down with Tsar Nicholas! Down with Tsar Nicholas!'

Avram is precise in his knowledge of historical details and dates, but whenever I am in doubt I retreat to libraries to fill in the gaps. I have been drawn into the hunt. I am engaged in reconstructing other times, other worlds.

On 9 January, in an incident that was to become known as Bloody Sunday, a procession of workers converged upon the winter palace in St Petersburg. They marched, two hundred thousand strong, bearing icons and portraits of the Tsar. They trudged through the snow, in search of an audience with their *Batyushka,* their revered Father, the emperor of all the Russias. They surged into the palace square, unarmed, singing anthems, led by a rebellious priest.

A cordon of troops barred their way. Horses strained at the bit. A sudden hail of bullets rent the crisp winter air. In their thousands the marchers ran, from the frenzied charge of cavalry. In panic they fled, from the batons and bayonets of militiamen. In their hundreds they fell, under the hooves of crazed horses, in a tangle of chaos and fear. The bloodstained corpses of men, women and children lay in the snow. Bullet-riddled images of the Tsar were scattered over the square. The social fabric was in tatters, countless lives torn to shreds. And never again would those who marched trust their *Batyushka.*

The spirit of rebellion spread. A year of revolution engulfed the land. In February, Grand Duke Sergei, the Tsar's Moscow envoy, was assassinated in his carriage, as he drove through the Kremlin gates. Peasants turned on their masters and seized their estates. Industrial workers closed down factories and surged out on a general strike. Soldiers mutinied in Vladivostok and Tashkent. And in June, whilst on manoeuvres in the Black Sea, the crew of the battleship *Potemkin* turned upon their officers.

The admiral in charge of the ship ordered the rebels to be shot. The firing squad refused to obey. The crew seized the squad's weapons, rushed their officers, threw some overboard, and locked the remainder in their cells. The *Potemkin* sailed into Odessa harbour flying the red flag. And on the morrow, Etta Stock, now a trained nurse, was sent on board to tend the crew, while rioting workers fought street battles, and the city was engulfed in flames.

'Now you understand?' exclaims a triumphant Avram. 'My mother was a legend! A maker of history! A revolutionary! As too was my father Yankel, the son of Alter Zeleznikow the lumberjack.'

Avram speaks with obvious pride. The son recalls the father, who begets the grandfather, and Alter Zeleznikow is reborn.

In the early years of this century, Alter would stand astride a flotilla of logs, which he guided along the River Pina from the city of Pinsk to the confluence of the River Dnieper. Hundreds of kilometres south he floated, upon the Dnieper's fast-flowing currents. On the banks hovered cathedrals with onion-shaped domes. In nearby fields huddled villages graced with thatch-roofed homes. In the distance loomed solitary farmhouses hewn out of stone, as the flotilla drifted downstream towards the Black Sea coast.

'Avramel,' interjects Masha. 'You are straying again. We will never reach the end of it!'

Masha moves from language to language with ease. She speaks Yiddish to Avram, addresses the waiters in Polish, consults the cafe-manager in Russian, greets her new guests in English, and converses with her friends in a fluid mixture of all four. As for the cabbage soup steaming in front of me, it is based on a recipe Masha gleaned from her mother.

'In Poland I would never have believed that one day I would be recreating my mother's dishes in a restaurant called Scheherazade,' she muses. 'I never imagined that one day I would cook for a living. Or that I would become a restaurateur. I always thought I would be a doctor. A professional. I studied medicine for three years. I studied medicine until the day I was forced to flee.'

Avram ignores Masha's comments. His mind is fixed upon the distant past like a man obsessed. He takes up the narrative where he left off, in 1905, the year of the first revolution, the year in which fifteen-year-old Yankel, Alter the lumberjack's son, was drawn into the secret cells of the Bund in Pinsk.

Yankel joined his elder brother, Shlomo, the commander of a band of vigilantes whose task it was to defend the Jewish quarters from anti-Semitic attacks. The year of rebellion was drawing to an end. The revolutionaries were a spent force. Tsarist troops crushed the lingering resistance with ruthless ease. Jews were singled out as 'enemies of Christ' and fomenters of civil unrest. Another wave of pogroms engulfed the townlets of White Russia and the Ukraine.

Uncle Shlomo fled for his life across a succession of borders to the port of Marseilles and, weeks later, sailed into New York harbour. He gazed with longing at the Statue of Liberty, stared in awe at the city's skyline, negotiated his way through the turnstiles of Ellis Island, and emerged into the crowded streets of the Lower East Side, where a job in a run-down sweatshop set him on the road to wealth and pride.

As for Yankel, he could flee only as far as the outskirts of Pinsk, where he took refuge in a hideout, a forest retreat. And waited, marking time, as he prepared for the next swelling of the revolutionary tide.

I glance round the cafe. A waitress tends the late-night guests. She is middle-aged, dressed in a black mini-skirt, black stockings, and a white blouse. Her perfume hovers in the air as she hurries by. A couple, bound within an aura of intimacy, gaze into each other's eyes. Several old men are ebbing towards sleep. A young man sits alone, and reads *A Treatise on Boredom*. He bites into a slice of cheesecake, washes it down with coffee, and all the while he is engrossed in his treatise on boredom.

I glance back at the ever-present Masha. On the table stand our stale teas, and half-eaten pastries.

'It is a miracle how couples meet,' Avram says, as if awakening from a trance. 'We are the children of accidents. Of random encounters. Take Yankel and Etta. It is a marvel how they met.'

Avram pours another glass of red. Pauses. And resumes his chronicle in 1908, the year in which Etta Stock journeyed on a mission, 250 kilometres north, from her native Tulchin to Berdichev: a city celebrated for its cantors and scribes, Hasidic dynasties and spiritual guides. A city where biblical Hebrew flowed from eighty prayer houses, the enduring language of a wandering tribe. A city where Yiddish coursed through the courtyards and market places, and emerged as the language of daily life. A city of trade workers and hired labour, where the Bund was able to regroup after the debacle of 1905.

Etta approached the seasoned leaders of the Berdichev Bund. She required their support in her efforts to kindle the flame of revolution back home in Tulchin. In response to Etta's request the party sent Yankel Zeleznikow. A good ten years younger than Etta, at eighteen Yankel was already a seasoned cadre and union organiser. In Tulchin Yankel boarded with Etta's family. In time, they became lovers. And by 1910 Etta was expecting a child.

Avram tells the tale matter-of-factly. And he is moving fast. I would like to know more about the romance. But Avram is concerned with data, with documenting his parents' heroic deeds in the erratic ebb and flow of history; and he is well prepared for the task. He reaches into his satchel. He covers the table with pamphlets and letters, journals and books, and photocopies of the Yiddish *Folkszeitung*, the Bund newspaper, announcing the marriage of party comrades Yankel Zeleznikow and Etta Stock.

Neither marriage nor pregnancy slowed the pace of the couple's work for a revolution they believed was pre-ordained. Yankel resumed his activity in the factories of the Ukraine. He urged workers to strike for better conditions, higher pay. One strike veered out of control; a gendarme was killed. The factory owner accused Yankel of the crime. Yankel was arrested and imprisoned in Pinsk. Etta was imprisoned in the nearby city of Kobrin; and it was in prison that their first child, a daughter named Basia, was born.

Avram points to the letters. He extracts a yellowing page. The Hebraic script, penned by Yankel in a prison cell, within days of his arrest, is all but impossible to comprehend.

The letter is addressed to his brother Shlomo in New York. Avram knows the contents well. Yankel agonises over his predicament. Should a revolutionary rear a family? he asks. When would I have time for a child? For the care and love she needs? And how will the family survive now that I have been sentenced to fifteen years labour so far removed from home?

Etta was released from prison after serving six months; but Yankel was exiled to a Siberian work camp near the city of Irkutsk, on the shores of Lake Baikal. In winter it glistened white, a boundless sheet of compressed ice. In spring it melted into an inland sea of billowing snow. In summer the horizon linked lake and sky in one seamless vista of bleached blues. In the autumn, cold winds heralded another season of stagnant twilights and gale-swept nights.

Yankel laboured and longed for the day when he would return to his grand obsession. Etta journeyed in his wake, thousands of kilometres east, with her new-born daughter, to Irkutsk. She obtained work as a nurse, looked after her infant child, and visited Yankel on the shores of Lake Baikal.

'She always carried the family on her shoulders,' says Avram. 'She was always both a breadwinner and revolutionary. She tended her husband, her children, her patients, and her comrades. She made time for everyone.'

'And Yankel?'

'He was a professional revolutionary. The party always came first. When I was a child I rarely saw him. He was often absent at night, at a meeting, a conference, a Bund gathering. Sometimes he was away for weeks on end, on missions throughout Poland. He was always on the move, always organising and scheming. When he was in town he would visit me at school, in the mornings, and treat me to breakfast. This was our allotted time together. Of him it was said: "Where he stands he talks, where he sits, he sleeps."'

'You are jumping ahead now,' Masha warns. 'One minute we are in Siberia, in Irkutsk, on Lake Baikal, ten years before you were born, and now we are in Vilna, twenty years later. Martin will be confused.'

But I do not mind. I enjoy the asides. The hours flow through the winter night. Trams glide by, like whispers on wheels. Lights wink from restaurants lining the street. A gentle rain slants down in transparent sheets. And Avram's lilting voice draws me back through the early years of a passing century.

In 1914, Archduke Ferdinand was assassinated in Sarajevo. The tribes of Europe converged upon the battlefields. In the millions they fell, foot soldiers in the service of emperors whose dominions were about to be swept aside. In muddy trenches, amid the stench of decaying flesh, their bodies numb with fatigue, they battled over mere metres of ground. And wherever they fought, they sowed the unmarked graves of countless wasted lives, until those who still remained screamed: 'Enough! Let the empire crumble! Let the old order die. We want bread! We want peace!'

In March 1917, Tsar Nicholas was swept aside; and thousands of kilometres to the east, on the shores of Lake Baikal, Yankel Zeleznikow was pardoned and released from his Siberian exile.

Towards the west they journeyed, Etta and Yankel, anxious to rekindle their life's work. They chose Kiev, capital of the Ukraine, as the city in which to resume their lives. They entered a city draped in red banners and flags. It was the alluring spring-time of revolution. A time of soap-box orators, fiery speeches, messianic visions. Fatigued villagers streamed in from the provinces lured by the promise of better days.

But it was short-lived, this interlude of utopian fantasies. The White Armies were on the march throughout the Ukraine. In August 1919, the Red Army retreated from Kiev. Battles raged on the banks of the River Dnieper. Thugs and bandits gained control of the streets.

Events seemed to be careering out of control. The Red Army regained the city in December. Typhus and famine engulfed the land. Revolution gave way to repression. The Red dictatorship took hold, the all-powerful party seized total control; and in 1922 the Bund was banned. Avram's father became a wanted man.

Yankel farewelled his wife and daughter, and fled Kiev in a horse-drawn wagon crowded with books. Russian novelists, French philosophers, Yiddish poets and socialist pamphleteers kept him company as he travelled west, through Poland, in search of yet another home. Wherever he went he was feted by Bund comrades and put up in the homes of fellow cadres. Wherever he journeyed he was assigned urgent missions.

Yankel's life became one extended detour that did not end until he arrived in Vilna. It was in the Jerusalem of Lithuania that Etta and Yankel were reunited, and finally set up a permanent home. And it was in this fabled city where, in 1924, their second child, Avram, was born.

II

Like a magnet Scheherazade draws them, cynics and idealists, ageing schemers and dreamers. One by one they enter on a Sunday morning. A typical Sunday. Each newcomer is greeted with a wave of the hand, a raised eyebrow, a familiar routine.

'Sholem Aleichem!'

'Aleichem Sholem!'

'Well? How is it going?'

'As you can see, I am still alive.'

'And how are the children?'

'They are so busy I have to make an appointment to see them.'

'And the business?'

'The business? It's deep in the ground.'

'So? That is where we will all be soon enough.'

Rapid-fire conversations echo from all corners of the cafe. Caffeine courses through the veins. The talk becomes louder, more animated. The chairs extend outwards as the circles expand.

Listen, and you will hear four, five, six voices at a time. Perhaps you think this impolite, lacking in manners, in style. But for those who participate this is a weekly *simkhe*, a celebration, a communal gathering. The babble of voices is an aria to their ears. A full-blown opera, first heard in the towns of their youth, in shtetl cottages, in crowded apartments with whole families packed together in one room.

To be heard was to learn to leap into a discussion, to dart in and out of an argument, to know when to deliver a punchline, an aphorism, a retort, while at the same time keeping an ear upon two, three, four simultaneous conversations, lest a crucial piece of gossip should pass one by.

They are like a chorus in a Greek drama, those who frequent Scheherazade on this winter morning. They fill in the gaps. They echo the central text. Each one has a story aching to be told: tales of townlets and cities now vanished from the earth, of journeys in search of refuge, a shelter from a curse.

Yossel Bartnowski enters the cafe with slow, measured steps. A man in his late eighties, he is well dressed for his Sunday promenade. He wears a pin-striped suit, double-breasted. A green umbrella dangles on his left arm. The umbrella matches his green shirt studs and emerald bow tie. His body is short and stocky, and suggests a tenacious will. His ample face falls away into a succession of chins. A red pullover highlights his red complexion; his braised cheeks are on fire with age. Yet, as he seats himself beside me, I am startled when I see that his eyes are an unblemished blue.

'My foolish child, age does not matter. Willpower can defeat it,' he tells me. 'I can still lift fifty kilos. I walk fifteen kilometres a day. I do not take short cuts. I do not waste time. I climb the stairs to my apartment. I set my heart to work. I pump the blood through my varicose veins. I leave the car rotting in the garage, and I walk until I burst.

'You are the writer, Martin Davis, no? I have read your articles in the press. I have read your stories about the old world, *der alter velt*. My foolish child, what do you understand about the past? You did not live there, may my enemies have such luck. What do you know of such things? You are still a young man. You were born here, in Australia, in a fortunate hour. If you wish to know *der alter velt*, I will tell you. If you wish to write about Vilna, you have hit the mark.

'My dear Martin, no one knows this city as well as I do: the central market place, the Sage of Vilna's house, the synagogue courtyard, the boulevards and lanes. I can still see them in front of my eyes. And I can see the hill, by the banks of the river, with the three crosses burning at night. And the rise on the opposite banks, with Count Gedimin's castle ruins; of course I knew that too. It was the perfect place to take a girl at night. Such a beautiful view. Such a beautiful girl. What a *mekhaiye*, a pure delight.

'And I know the history. You think I am an ignoramus? Vilna was founded by Count Gedimin; six, maybe seven hundred years ago, give or take a century or two. What does it matter? It was a long time ago. I know the poem, 'Pan Tadeusz' by Mickiewicz. I learnt it as a child. I can still recite it by heart. In the original Polish, of course!'

And Yossel declaims with a flourish:

'Gedimin, by meandering Wilja's and Wilenka's streams,
Lay, bewitched, while he dreamed of the iron wolf;
And awakened by the gods' command,
Built Vilna like a wild wolf that breeds
In the forest among bears, boars and bison.

'You see, my dear Martin? I am not an ignoramus. But a poem is just a poem. If you wish to know a city, you must sit in its cafes. This is the most important thing to do when you arrive in a new place. This is where you sniff the air, and know what is what.

'In Vilna, if you wanted to know what was happening, you went to Wolfke's. If you wanted to make contacts, do business, where else would you go but Wolfke's? If you wanted to forget your worries, to hear a story, a joke, the best place was Wolfke's.

'It stood on the corner of Niemecka and Zydowska. Just one hop and a spring from the synagogue courtyard. First I would pray, and then I would run to Wolfke's for a bite, a quick drink! My foolish child, Wolfke's was the Scheherazade of Vilna.'

Yossel orders a coffee. It remains untouched as his eyes scan the cafe. He is expecting his regular companions, Laizer Bialer and Zalman Grintraum. They share the same miracle, Yossel tells me. They first met in Wolfke's, in the final months of 1939. The city was inflated with refugees. They clogged community buildings, the synagogue foyers, private apartments, and single rooms. From every corner of Nazi-controlled Poland they had fled, from Lublin and Lodz, from Siedlce, Krakow and Belz, from Chelm and Czestochova, from every village and town, from every alley and avenue on which their families had once lived.

Yossel too had fled to Vilna, from his native Warsaw, where he was raised. Krochmalna Street was his cradle. Its crumbling courtyards were his playgrounds. A ground-floor apartment was the family home. In the apartment next door lived a family of thieves, and on an upper floor there was a school for thieves, where thirteen-year-old boys would gather to learn how to pick pockets. Their teachers were professional crooks.

'My foolish child, do you think they had a choice?' says Yossel. 'It was a family enterprise. The mother looked after the stolen goods. She kept an inventory. She was the boss; a big woman who could hardly squeeze through a narrow door. *Freidl die fresserin*, she was called. Freda the guts. She could eat a whole goose at one sitting. She dealt in geese. She would stride through the streets of Warsaw with a goose tucked firmly under each arm while bands of children followed her chanting: *"Freidl die fresserin. Freidl die fresserin."*'

Yossel tells this story often, to anyone who is willing to listen, who allows him the slightest chance. Yossel still stalks the streets of Warsaw. He still hovers in its shadows. He remains obsessed by a world of hoodlums and fear.

'We roamed the neighbourhood in gangs: the Polacks versus the Yids. Each gang had its territory, its exclusive beat. Our leader was Mendel Mandelbaum. He was the strongest Yid in Krochmalna Street. He was a porter. An ox. He could carry a safe on his shoulders. He led a gang of porters and wagon drivers. They fought many battles until Mendel Mandelbaum and the Yids prevailed and, for a few months, peace descended upon Krochmalna Street.

'Mendel was my protector. I followed him wherever I could. I followed him to the Polonia, the biggest and best hotel in Warsaw. We would go down to the basement cafe, where the boys from Krochmalna played billiards and pool.

'Mendel played for high stakes. He would bet one hundred zlotys on a single game. He played against a highly ranked government official. A crowd of onlookers watched them compete. The boys from Krochmalna placed their hard-earned zlotys on Mendel. Others put their money on his opponent. There was always an even chance of winning or losing, so closely were they matched.

'But danger was never far away. Violence could erupt at any time, even as we played in the basement cafe behind the broad shoulders of our Mendel. My foolish child, what do you know about danger? About fear? Here we live in a paradise!

'Stanislaw the pimp would descend into the cafe surrounded by a gang of henchmen. He had the most beautiful women working for him. Stanislaw was the king of the pimps. His face was scarred all over from knife cuts he had received in the many street battles he fought until he emerged on top of the heap.

'We all feared him. Martin, how can you know what is fear? In Australia we have no fear. Here we live in a *gan eiden*, a golden land. We make a living. We educate our children. I have one daughter, a chemist, a second daughter, a doctor; and a son-in-law, a professor of literature. A true *goan*. A sage. He knows all the great books of the world. And he knows nothing. I am joking, of course. He is a clever boy.'

Yossel is breathless. His heart is pumping. And this pleases him. It makes him feel he is fully alive. He reaches for his wallet and extracts two photos.

'My grandchildren,' he announces. 'This is my true wealth. My legacy. My pride. Here we made a good life.' Yossel sweeps his arm in an arc to include the old men and sprinkling of women bent over their coffees at the tables of Scheherazade.

'Stanislaw the pimp advanced towards us, his arms hanging by his sides. My dear Martin, of course I was afraid! I was terrified. I wanted to run to the toilet. I was shaking inside and out. Even now, sixty years later, I cannot understand why I ran out in front of Stanislaw with an ashtray in my hand. How could I do such a foolish thing? I was possessed. I was moved by a *meshugene* impulse, a sudden rage.

'I hurled the ashtray at Stanislaw. I can see it now, as it flew towards him. I can see the exact moment when it crashed against his forehead. I can see the skin breaking open, the blood squirting over his face. I can see his astonishment, his burning eyes, as he leapt at me, clawed at me like a wounded animal. By the time Mendel came to my aid, Stanislaw had landed enough blows to send me to hospital for a month.

'When I returned I was the toast of the streets. This is how it was. The boys of Krochmalna put on a reception for me. The

Polish and Jewish underworld joined together to welcome me back. They hired the banquet hall of the Polonia.

'"Let bygones be bygones," they said. Stanislaw and his henchmen gave me their hand. We recalled our battles like old soldiers at a reunion. We dined on gefilte fish and caviar. We sipped coffee and liqueurs. We toasted each other with cognac. The best quality. All stolen, of course. "Do not trifle with Yossel," my former enemies said. I was welcomed back a hero.'

'A hero in underpants!' interjects Laizer Bialer as he seats himself at the table, without the merest hint of small talk, an 'excuse me', or a polite aside. 'That no-good bastard is telling you about Krochmalna? That scoundrel is boasting about his great deeds? Always the same story. Always Krochmalna. Always poverty. Always Mendel and Stanislaw. We know his grandmothers' tales by heart.'

Laizer's face is gaunt, his cheeks sunken, his eyes constantly on the move, absorbed in everything about him. He radiates a desperate zest for life, as if any moment lost would be a small death in itself. He dresses plainly in slacks, an open-necked shirt, a well-worn tweed jacket. As he talks his forehead furrows in concentration. His oval-shaped face alternates between wariness and unexpected warmth. He veers between a hard clipped Yiddish and English, which he speaks with the old-fashioned correctness of someone who has mastered it late in life.

'You no-good scribbler,' he says, turning to me. 'Yes, I know who you are. I have seen your columns, God help us. I have read your foolish stories, may my enemies be so clever. So, now you want to write about Vilna? And about Wolfke's? Where we did meet, Yossel, Zalman and I? I will tell you how it was, without Yossel's embellishments and lies.'

Zalman has glided into our presence. His face is somewhat softer, reflective, as if troubled, as if trying to discern a deeper truth which still awaits him, just beyond reach. He is the most reticent of the three, and thinner, more compact, more youthful-looking, even though, like Laizer, he is almost eighty. His neatly cut hair has not turned fully grey. He is dressed in a pair of jeans, a checked shirt, and sneakers. His clothes are well fitting, yet casual and loose.

'Ah, the intellectual has finally arrived,' says Laizer with a hint of sarcasm.

They are very different, our three friends, the refined Zalman, the streetwise Yossel, and the belligerent Laizer with his ironic smile. Yet the bond between them is palpable, an indelible friendship first forged in the Vilna of the Red interlude, a city full of foreboding.

'I can still see it clearly,' says Laizer. 'Over the door there was a sign, written in Yiddish: Wolfke's. Outside, on Zydowska Street, would gather porters and peddlers, wagon drivers and chauffeurs. While their horses stood by water-troughs and drank, their masters filed into the saloon for a whisky, a snack.

'The saloon was the outer room. The floor was covered in sawdust. A bartender poured mugs of beer, a brandy, any concoction one desired. Sometimes a fight would break out; and just as quickly it would be broken up. There was always something happening in the bar.

'Those with more money hurried through to the restaurant. The tables were crowded with families rich enough to eat out. It was like Scheherazade will be in an hour or so, when people come for their Sunday lunch. They stuffed themselves, fought over politics, traded jokes, boasted about their business deals, spoilt their children with sweets, and gossiped until their throats creaked,' concludes Laizer, with a triumphant smile.

'In Wolfke's you could get the best Sabbath cholent in Vilna,' enthuses Yossel. 'Such a mouth-watering stew! So thick with potatoes and chunks of meat. And, for a snack, you could order a beautiful chopped liver. It was a *mekhaiye.* A pure delight. With beaten onion and egg, floating in chicken fat.'

'So, you no-good bastard, you Krochmalna Street know-all. Any mention of food and your mouth drools,' retorts Laizer. 'But, I must admit, on this subject you do know what you are talking about. And, if you wanted to fill your belly with delicacies, you could go to the banquet hall, where there did gather bohemians and dandies with their hangers-on. And no-good intellectuals like our friend Zalman, forever boasting that they knew how to change the world. Here we did come after an evening at the cinema for a vodka and an argument.'

'And for the beautiful girls,' interjects Yossel. 'In Wolfke's we could dance, to the radio, a quick tango. Ah. What a *mekhaiye*!'

'*Nu*, not only are you a hero in underpants, but a Casanova!' says Laizer. 'Yes, we did dance on the bare wooden floors. And we ate finely cut salami and goose feet. We snacked on gefilte fish, peppered, Vilna-style. We feasted on pickled herring and boiled beef. We partied until daybreak and stumbled out bloated into Zydowska Street.'

As Laizer holds forth, Zalman is humming. His eyes are fixed on some distant point. His humming becomes discernible, a melody, a Yiddish song. Laizer and Yossel fall silent. Around them the world is beginning to burn. And in the distance can be heard the trembling of forests, the cries of marauders, the tread of a sinister enemy approaching the city gates:

'I searched for you all over town,
Except for the one cellar where you waited.
That is my fate, oh my fate.
I searched for you throughout the world
With your image always dancing before me,
But nowhere were you to be found.
So I sat down, heavy-hearted, on a stone,
Yet your image still hovered before me
Always in the distance, just beyond reach.
To search and never find is a terrible burden;
To search without end is a terrible fate.'

As Zalman sings I glance at the tables: on each table a rectangular beige mat, on each mat a glass ashtray, and containers of sugar, pepper and salt. A ray of late-morning sun lights up the objects, and for a brief moment they seem like antidotes to ageing men, burdened with memories which will never be erased.

'September 1939 was the month that changed our fate,' says Zalman. 'Blue skies were muddied by planes that spat misery into our lives. In Warsaw, I saw buildings split and craters opening before my eyes. I decided to flee the city I had lived in all my life. I hugged my loved ones and took to the roads as though pursued by rabid dogs. I leapt under bushes as though they could protect us from bombs. I ran through forests crackling with flames. I saw the bark peeling from trees ablaze. And still I ran.

'I fled past overturned wagons, as their owners scattered for their lives. I ran in a frenzy past the injured and dead. I leapt over wounded horses shrieking in agony. I slipped in and out of barns. I hid in sewers and drains. I jumped on and off moving trains. I waded across rivers and streams. I saw town lights in the distance, and made my way through the Vilna gates. And I found temporary respite in a city bursting with refugees.

'It would take some time before I realised that it would be the first of many cities which seemed, from a distance, to be the haven I craved. It would take years to accept I would never see my loved ones again. It would take decades before I fully understood that to search without end is a terrible fate.'

Zalman lapses back into silence. Yossel and Laizer remain still. For a moment we are disoriented, unable to move until, as abruptly as it had begun, the spell is broken, and the tumult is upon us again. Families are entering for their midday meals. Waitresses are rushing between the tables. Avram and Masha have arrived and sit at the back table, checking the mounting bills.

Zalman, Yossel and Laizer retreat. The old men are spilling out onto the street. They cannot quite let go of each other's company. They linger against lampposts and parked cars, or stand in the middle of the pavement, unaware of passers-by. Sunday is reaching out for the afternoon, but they persist with their opinions as if to argue is to know they are alive. They continue to tell their tales, as if to talk is to know they have survived.

III

In Acland Street, not so long ago, there was one cafe. Perhaps two. Now every month new cafes appear, like mushrooms sprouting after autumn rain. Each one boasts its distinctive appeal. Just stroll the length of one full block, the crucial block, from Shakespeare Grove to Barkly Street. They stand side by side, with menus pasted on plate-glass windows, proclaiming their riches like spruikers at a country fair.

The range is overwhelming: from the Cosmo to La Roche, from the Blue Danube to the Espresso Bar. Stop for a moment in Deveroli's, a supermarket of a cafe, with enough chairs to seat a battalion of coffee connoisseurs. Adjust your sunglasses and saunter into Cafe Manna or Cafe Mondo, Cicciolina or the Zenith Bar. Sit at a pavement table in the morning sun. Or join the boys outside the Pit Stop burger shop for a meal on the run.

Acland Street is raining caffeine. Of every conceivable variety and form: short black, flat white, froth-topped Viennese, raw Turkish, roughly ground. Or is it Bulgarian? Or Greek? Wars have been fought over that one.

Not to be left behind, Le Bon cake shop has concocted its very own 'cocktail' brew. 'Experience something new in coffee,' a window poster proclaims. 'With over 40 varieties,' from ice-cooled lattes for the midday heat to whisky-spiked Irish for a wintry night.

I stroll past this maze of cafes, and make my way to Scheherazade. It is weeks since I last entered, and spring has finally arrived. As I wait at the back table for Avram and Masha to finish their chores, I jot down notes. It is my habit, a journalist's curse. 'Each cafe begets another,' I write, 'and for every coffee shop on Acland Street I imagine a precursor, a cafe of the mind. Such as Wolfke's, which once stood in the city of Vilna, on the corner of Niemecka and Zydowska streets.'

'I knew it well,' says Avram, after he and Masha join me. 'My father would take me there as a special treat. We descended into a large room with wooden tables. It was always in a tumult, a chaotic mess. Everyone seemed to be shouting and smoking. It was a favourite meeting place for my father's Bundist mates.

'There were many such places in Vilna. In the same court-yard stood Levanda's vegetarian restaurant; and around the corner the Cafe Prater, where Yiddish journalists would gather to eat. On elegant Mickiewicz Street stood *Die Grinne Shtral,* The Green Ray. This cafe was more refined. Here we would stroll on a Sunday afternoon, for coffee and cake.

'And there was Dorman's on Broad Street, where a women's orchestra would perform; and nearby stood the Palais de Danse, where string bands played night after night. Vilna's dance halls were always full. Vilna was a world full of little worlds. It possessed all that the heart desired, and the stomach required. But it all came to nothing; it all came to a bitter end.'

Avram is quickly back into the momentum of history. He is not a man for the intricacies of social life. I want to know more about the streets that once flowed with caffeine and cake. But Avram was taught to see the world as a theatre of grand movements, a clash of epic forces. In one leap he moves away from Wolfke's to the defining moment:

'In Vilna we thought we were safe. We thought the Nazi–Soviet pact, signed in August '39, would protect us. At least this is what my father believed. "The Red Army will soon arrive," he predicted. "There will be no need to run. There is no need to be afraid of the Bolsheviks. We may have different points of view, but we belong to the same movement. After all, we are fighting a common enemy."'

Avram inscribes circles as he speaks. He clutches his forehead. He clenches his fists. His hands are the subtext; his clenched fists are clenched emotions. His wrinkled forehead is a straining for memory. His measured words an attempt to circumscribe time.

'To understand the fate of my father,' he says, 'we must return to the city of Pinsk, the birthplace of my father's father, Alter the lumberjack. Pinsk was then part of Poland. It was located near its eastern borders, still beyond reach of the invading Germans. You must understand this was an insane part of the world, a battleground of rival tribes. Countries often changed hands overnight. It had always been like this. Both

Vilna and Pinsk were occupied by the Bolsheviks, for short periods, after World War I, but in 1920, they were annexed by Poland. As for the Lithuanians, they still longed for independence and regarded Vilna as their ancient capital.

'In the early days of September '39, my father sent me to an uncle and aunt who lived in Pinsk. He wanted to be free of the family at this time. He had many things on his mind. He had urgent matters to deal with. The Third Reich was on the march.

'I travelled with my sister Basia, and her two-year-old son, Shmulek, the first grandchild. I was fifteen. Pinsk is perhaps two hundred kilometres south of Vilna. We arrived on the eve of Rosh Hashonah, the New Year. My pious uncle told me my father would always accompany him to the recital of prayers on Rosh Hashonah, even though he was a non-believer. I was expected to follow the tradition.

'After we entered the synagogue, I did not know what to do. I stood with a prayer book in hand, and felt like a fool. I could not even follow the service. I did not understand the Hebrew text. I was surrounded by men in prayer-shawls who glanced at me with contempt. In their eyes I was an ignoramus, a boy who had gone astray. I felt ashamed. I ran from the shul. I fled to the home of Aaron Yudel Schlakhman, the leader of the Bund in Pinsk.

'Aaron was one of my childhood heroes. He was a close friend of my father's, and had visited our Vilna apartment. I was in awe of his battle scars. He had lost an arm in the revolution of 1905. He was an anarchist in those days. His arm was blown off by a bomb. He was assembling the parts when it exploded. Two years later he abandoned his anarchist ways and became an ardent member of the Bund.

'I ran to his house. Here I would be among comrades. Here I would feel at home. The rooms were crowded with Bund leaders in flight from western and central Poland. They had arrived, just days earlier. I was the youngest, privileged to be among legends; such as Noiakh, a founder of the Bund. He was one of a small band of revolutionaries who secretly met in a house in Vilna, in 1897, to form the new movement. I could not believe I was in his company.

'The next day I was entrusted with my first mission. I was to find my way to a village, twenty kilometres distant. I was to make contact with Henryk Erlich, a renowned Bund leader, and his wife Sofia. They had both escaped from German-occupied Warsaw. I was to escort them back to Pinsk, where it was hoped the Polish government might regroup and fight back.

'I travelled by horse and wagon. We approached a bridge over the Pina, on the outskirts of Pinsk, the river on which Alter the lumberjack once guided logs on the first leg of his journeys to the Black Sea. Polish soldiers guarding the bridge warned that I might not get back. The bridge was mined. The Red Army was approaching.

'I remember that moment clearly. It was the moment of my first big decision. My first independent decision. Somehow I knew it would be the first of many decisions which would be matters of life and death.

'I decided to go ahead. We stole across the bridge to the village in which the Erlichs were hiding, about five kilometres away. And we returned just in time. Hours later the bridge was blown up and, the next day, the Red Army marched into Pinsk. They also attacked by river, with troops that had sailed all the way from the Black Sea. The city was in chaos.

'I remained in Aaron's house with Erlich. His comrades fetched a barber to cut off his beard. They wanted him to change his appearance. He was in danger from the Bolsheviks, they claimed.

'"From the Bolsheviks I do not hide," Erlich replied. It wasn't that he trusted them. He was well aware of the purges, the Stalinist terror, the show trials, the Siberian camps. But now that the Red Army was advancing, now that the Nazis were destroying Poland, we would all unite against a common enemy, he reasoned. Whatever has happened in the past, we still come from the same family, the same roots.

'This was also my father's thinking. This is what he told me when I returned to Vilna, weeks later. By then, as he had predicted, the Red Army occupied the city. As in Kiev, two decades earlier, the buildings were draped in red banners, the streets festooned with red flags. My father was about to flee Vilna, but when he saw the Bolsheviks marching through the streets he changed his mind. Surely they would form a united front. After all, they were all revolutionaries, united in a common cause. After all, he had done time in Siberia, on the frozen shores of Lake Baikal.'

Avram strokes his chin, then brushes a hand across his eyes. He sees armies on the march, villages ablaze. He sees the clash of dictators, the clash of ideas, and the sprouting of tears. The roads of Europe were littered with betrayals. Avram recalls the fierce arguments between Bund comrades. Anna Rosenthal was the leader of the Vilna Bund at the time. 'The same legendary Anna who had participated in the "Romanov uprising" of 1904, in eastern Siberia,' Avram tells me, with his customary gleam of pride.

'Avramel? Where are you taking us now?' interrupts Masha. 'This is another story.'

'Yes, it is another story,' Avram replies. 'But it is important that Martin understands Anna Rosenthal was a woman of great courage, with an honourable past. Someone who would not let down her friends; a woman who, in Tsarist times, had spent years in Siberian jails. Yet it was the same Anna Rosenthal who, just after the Bolsheviks marched into Vilna, went to the offices of the NKVD, the Soviet secret police, and supplied them with lists of Bund members. She did it in good faith. They were allies, the police assured her. They required the names and addresses so that they could be contacted in times of need. Even then we were still naive.

'A week later, Anna was arrested, as too were many of her comrades. My father was forewarned. A friend had seen his name on the police lists. His arrest was imminent. His comrades urged him to leave with them, immediately.

'"Me? Yankel Zeleznikow? Arrested by the Bolsheviks?"

father replied. "So what! I am not afraid of them."

'He stayed put. And they came at midnight to our apartment on Benedictinski 4, in the old quarters of Vilna. This had been our home for the past ten years, our one bit of security after a lifetime on the run. Mother loved the apartment. It was a three-storey building and we lived on the ground floor. We even had a mahogany piano. My sister Basia was a concert pianist. She had graduated from the Vilna conservatory. Music was in the family. After all, Avram Stock, my mother's father, was once a fiddler, a lifelong player in a klezmer band.

'Have I told you this story? My mother had a brother called Jonah, who also played the violin; he was a member of the Leningrad symphony orchestra, but he too disappeared during the Stalinist purges. Sooner or later, they all disappeared.'

'Avramel,' interrupts Masha, 'where in this bitter world are you taking us now? Please, concentrate at least for a moment on Benedictinski 4.'

'Yes, Benedictinski 4. I grew up with interesting neighbours. In the apartment opposite ours lived Reb Chaim Ozer Grodzinski. The rooms served as the *Beth Din,* Reb Ozer's rabbinical court. For years they had flocked to him, the believers, to receive his blessings, to sign marriage papers, arrange divorces, resolve squabbles. Reb Ozer sat day after day in a black caftan, stroking his white beard. He would sway from side to side whilst the litigants argued their case.

'He once called upon my father, even though Yankel was an avowed non-believer. This particular case could not be decided by rabbinical law, Reb Ozer told him. It required the help of someone well-versed in the laws of economics, and the demands of the secular world. Yankel was brought in to advise.

'The dispute concerned a factory owner and a worker who claimed he had not been adequately paid. It was a difficult case to decide. Since World War I, Vilna had become a city of great poverty. Beggars wandered the streets in packs. Children ran about in bare feet. The alleys were crowded with hovels where whole families slept on a single mattress or a pile of sacks.

'When Poland absorbed the city in 1920, it was cut off from its pre-war markets in Russia and in countries by the Baltic Sea. So, when it came to manufacturing, there was little money for either owner or worker.'

'Avramel!'

'Masha, *loz op*! It is important that Martin should know that Vilna was also a city of paupers. This is why there were so many peddlers, selling their rags on its poorer streets. This is why there were so many smugglers and black marketeers. Have I told you this story? There was a man whom everyone called Rasputin. No one seemed to know his real name. He was a giant of a man, with a long black beard, and an unkempt mane of wild hair. He could always be found in Wolfke's, drinking in the outer saloon.

'Like his namesake he was surrounded by many women. He ruled over them like a king. He was not a pimp, but a prince among beggars. In exchange for looking after them, the women would give him a cut of their earnings.

'Rasputin's women roamed the Jewish quarters from sunrise until dusk. Each woman had her territory, her assigned beat. They would go from house to house, through every alley, and, whether you gave them a donation or not, they would always leave you with the same blessing: *May you have, and may you give.*

'"So why the same blessing?" my father once asked him.

'"Ah! It is a blessing with two very different meanings," Rasputin replied. "If you are one of the givers, we bless you so that you should have more, and therefore be able to give more. And if you do not give, we bless you to have the good fortune to be sick, and be condemned to give out groans."'

'Tell Martin the story of your father's arrest,' exclaims Masha, 'or we will go insane.'

'They came at midnight,' murmurs Avram, 'the secret police. They searched our apartment. They interrogated my mother. They arrested my father. But he was well prepared. After all, he was a seasoned revolutionary. He had his overnight bag packed with essentials. He would be back within weeks, he assured us.

'I accompanied him to jail. My father was a heavy smoker. I slipped him several packets of cigarettes. He grasped my hands, kissed me goodbye, and disappeared through the prison gates. I never saw him again.

'Over the years we received reports. Glimpses. Crumbs of information from former comrades who had shared a cell, a prison yard. He had been sighted in a Siberian camp. He had been interrogated by the secret police. He had been beaten and severely bashed. The NKVD wanted him to write a book exposing the false ideals of the Bund. He had refused, so he remained in jail.

'Stalin was like the tsars of old. It was the same bitter wine, despite the new red bottles. Like Uncle Jonah, the fiddler, my father vanished in the labour camps of Siberia. So many vanished without trace.'

'My family did survive Siberia,' says Masha.

Until now, she has deferred to Avram's monologue. She has sat by his side, alert to his every word. 'Compared to Avram, I led a sheltered life,' she adds. 'Compared to Avram, my story is trivial. Compared to those who remained in Lithuania and Poland, we spent the war years in paradise. For many years, I thought my story was not worth telling.'

I glance at the glowing lamps, the ashtrays, the white serviettes laid out in readiness for the evening meal. I take in the counter display of the day's cakes: almond rings and apple-strudel, marzipan sticks and nougat delight. Behind the counter, the mirrored backdrop reflects a steady procession of customers disappearing into the St Kilda night. These are the touchstones, the props to a tale of a journey towards the Empire of the White Bears. A journey which began on a sunlit autumn day in September 1939.

They ran in fear. They ran for their lives. Twelve-year-old Masha, her mother, her younger sister and brother, from the Polish city of Sosnowiec. For the first of many times they were refugees, just four among the thousands who choked the single road which led out of town.

'Father had told us to run,' says Masha, 'and make our way to Siedlce, a shtetl hundreds of kilometres north-east of Sosnowiec. My parents, Josef and Yohevets Frydman, were born and raised in Siedlce. They were also Bundists. In the 1920s they had been sent to Sosnowiec to organise trade unions. Sosnowiec was a city in the south-west, and Siedlce was to be a stepping stone to the east, to the River Bug, the new border between Russia and Poland.

'Grandfather Hershl Frydman was a rabbi, a follower of the Bialer Hasidim. He spent his days in a *shtiebele*, a tiny prayer house in Siedlce, where he studied and taught Torah. He was known as Hershl "Mruk", the brooder, because he did not talk very much. He was upset with his four children. All of them had forsaken their religion. All had become trade unionists and revolutionaries. One of his daughters was a communist. She rose through the ranks to become the party secretary in Siedlce. She was a passionate woman. I was impressed by her independence. I liked the straightforward way she dealt with people. I wanted to be like her.

'And my father was also a renegade. When he was a young man he would deliberately go to the Siedlce synagogue, his head bared, on Yom Kippur, the holiest day of the year, a day of fasting and repentance; and he would stand on the steps, and eat; and my *bubbe* would try to keep the peace.

'"Yossel, please, if you must eat, can't you go and eat

somewhere else," she would plead. She was a gentle woman. She had reared twelve children of whom only four survived. In a crisis she was always there, always ready to provide shelter, a warm meal, a clean bed.

'In September 1939 we ran for Siedlce, for the comfort of our *bubbe* and *zeide.* We ran until we were surrounded, in a field. Everything was burning. Even the trees were on fire. But because we were children the German soldiers spared us. We returned to Sosnowiec. It was the first of many miracles.

'Two weeks later we set out again, this time by train, for Warsaw. Poland was under siege. I was afraid. And I was excited. I had been entrusted with a mission. Father told me to take charge. Mother remained silent because her Polish was heavily accented. She could be easily identified as a Jew. I was to do the talking. I loved the responsibility. I felt like an adult.

'In Warsaw we boarded a horse-drawn cart and continued our journey east. I was very proud of myself when we arrived in Siedlce. I had accomplished my mission.

'Father joined us one month later. He walked all the way from Sosnowiec. He walked by night, and hid by day. He walked in a hurry. He wanted only to move east, away from the advancing terror. After he arrived safely in Siedlce, he did not stop. He took the four of us under his wing and we set out for the east, for the safety of the Soviet empire.

'On New Year's Eve, we arrived at the border, on the banks of the River Bug. The water was frozen over. On the first day of 1940, we walked across the ice into Russia. In broad daylight.

The entire family. I will never forget it. I still dream about it. The sun was shining. The snow was high. It dripped from the skies. It hung from the trees. It clung to our clothes, while from afar there drifted the voices of Russian soldiers on patrol.

'They were singing a folk song. I can still hear it now, the harmony, the voices floating in the air. Anyone who has lived in Russia knows this song.' And Masha finds her way back to the words, which she recites haltingly, without the melody, in fragments of barely remembered verse:

'The apple and pear trees have blossomed;
The mist on the river has gone.
Katyusha has left for the riverbank,
To sing of the soldier she loves.
Oh heart-felt song of my longing,
Fly far on the rays of the sun.
Katyusha will cherish her precious love
Until her lover from war shall return.'

They walked for their lives. They walked with rucksacks on their backs. They walked until Masha's ten-year-old brother, Lonka, refused to go on. They stood in no man's land, between contending empires. The sun shone, the snow twinkled, the strains of a Russian folk song wafted upon a breeze.

Lonka sat on the ice and did not move. His parents pleaded. They threatened. They tugged at his arms. They were visible targets, fully exposed. They begged him, with mounting panic, until at last he allowed them to drag him back onto his feet.

They walked on through a wonderland engulfed in mist. They walked to the beat of their hearts, towards the beckoning east. They moved as fast as the ice would allow them. When they finally reached the opposite bank, they kissed the frozen earth. And when they came upon the patrol of Red Army soldiers, Josef Frydman bent down and kissed the commander's feet.

'We settled in the border town of Lutzk,' Masha continues. 'But our freedom was short-lived. The Soviet police came to our home, in the middle of the night. They battered the doors with batons and rifle butts. "*Bistro! Bistro!*" they screamed. "*Bistro! Bistro!* You have twenty minutes to pack. *Bistro! Bistro!*"'

'*Bistro* is a Russian word which was adapted by the French,' interrupts Avram. Such details fascinate him. 'When the victorious Russians came to Paris after the defeat of Napoleon, they would walk into restaurants and demand: "*Bistro! Bistro!* Quickly! Quickly! We want to eat. We are hungry; and we are busy. So make it quick." Because of this, *bistro* came to mean a place for a snack. Not like our Scheherazade where you can sit all afternoon over one cup of coffee.'

'Avramel, let me tell *my* story,' insists Masha. 'As I was saying, we had to be quick. We grabbed what we could. Clothes. Photos. Mementos. We descended into the street. "*Bistro! Bistro!*" We marched through the darkness, at gunpoint. We were "unwanted elements", nobodies. We were directed into cattle trucks. Fifty or so to a carriage. It all happened so quickly. We did not know where we were being taken. We had lost control over our fate.'

This is a tale of maps, both old and new. Maps with shifting borders, obsolete before the ink could dry. Maps that created bands of nomads, stateless refugees. Maps criss-crossed by trains shunting their cargoes of uprooted wanderers thousands of kilometres east, on a nine-week journey, over glacial plains and snow-capped ranges, through white nights and broken days, an interminable journey that came to an abrupt halt at a remote station.

Taiga forests swayed in the distance; fields of snow extended to the horizon; and in the foreground stood the wooden huts and dormitories of a *pasholik*, a desolate labour camp.

Masha recalls the welcoming speech of the camp commander. And his final words: 'You will get used to it. And if you don't, you will slowly die, like dogs.'

Hundreds did die like dogs, from disease and despair, from hunger and unbearable cold, or from the sheer vastness, from the blinding whiteness of snow. Prisoners would deliberately walk out into the darkness, and vanish. It was as if they had never existed. Or they would be brought back, days later, frozen to death, their rigid corpses a reminder to the living that they were ciphers within a void.

The Frydmans were among those who did get used to it.

Josef was assigned to a work brigade that felled trees and hauled timber. He disappeared into the forests with his fellow workers in the pre-dawn gloom, and returned exhausted, long after dark.

By day, Masha worked in the communal kitchen and, late at night, as the weary camp inmates slept, she would steal out with little Lonka, in search of potatoes. They dug them out with their gloved hands, from beneath the snow. As they worked they could hear the howling of wolves.

A settlement in Siberia. It was harsh. It was strangely beautiful. It was a wilderness. The prisoners inhaled ice. They were infested with lice. On fatigue-laced summer evenings, the shadows played over barren steppes. A Polish countess taught the young girls how to dance. She taught Masha the polka and czardas. She sewed dresses for her students and they performed the dances in a *pasholik* concert.

Masha enrolled in the village school. She trudged seven kilometres through snow every morning and afternoon. She walked in a world of silence, broken by sudden gusts of wind. She trekked through a world of white upon white. A *pasholik* in Siberia. The coming of age of a young girl. It was harsh. It was strangely beautiful. It was a wilderness.

'About this period alone, you could write a book,' says Masha.

And, not for the first time, I am overcome by an uneasy feeling that I am stranded in the snows of Siberia; trapped at a table in the back room of a cafe called Scheherazade.

In late September 1941, after almost two years of incarceration, the inmates were assembled by the *pasholik* commander to be informed they were now free. Two months earlier, a deal had been brokered in London between the Soviets and the Polish government-in-exile. The Red empire was now at war with the Third Reich. Polish citizens on the run in Russia were now regarded as allies rather than slaves.

Yet Masha does not recall a sense of celebration. She cannot recall a moment of departure, a sense of ending. The journey was far from over. All that had changed was the direction.

Move south, the freed prisoners reasoned. Move south, towards the sun, away from the northern winds. They gathered on railway platforms, sat in crowded waiting rooms. They slept on wooden benches. They dozed on sackcloth and stone floors. And waited. Endlessly they waited for the next train south. This was the thought that obsessed them: to reach the sun.

And when, at last, a place was secured, in a cattle wagon, the Frydmans were one family among thousands. They acquired the skill of sleeping on their feet. They learnt to leap out of slowing carriages by provincial stations to dash for water. They squatted on train tracks, or stood in dark corners to relieve themselves. They mastered the delicate art of defecating from the sides of moving wagons. And they clung to their simple goal: to move south. To Tashkent, 'the city of bread'. To Alma-Ata, the 'mother of apples'. Perhaps to Bukhara, 'the city of mosques'. To the Asiatic republics. To the sunlit extremities of an empire.

At long last they began to feel the changing winds, the scent of breezes which hinted at weightless days. At last they could fling off the burden of heavy clothes. The breezes flowed through the wagon doors and allowed them a brief respite.

The Frydmans alighted in Merke, a hamlet in southern Kazakhstan. There was work here, they had heard on the refugee grapevine. On the outskirts of the hamlet stood a sugar refinery and an enclave of factories. The men-folk had been drafted to fight in distant wars. Newcomers were welcomed through the factory doors.

Merke alternately sweltered and froze. Through its streets trudged the dispossessed: Poles and Uzbeks, Chechens and Kazakhs, Gypsies and Jews, in search of a home. When at last they secured one, they lived ten or more to a room.

The houses were of mudbrick, the alleys paved with clay. Summer winds whipped the fields into dust. Winter winds capped the nearby mountains with ice. The range stretched towards the Chinese border. Bandits roamed the forbidding terrain. They raided farms and village homes. They battled each other for limited spoils.

Masha acquired another language: Kazakh. She trekked to village markets to sell the shoes her father had stolen from his place of work, and dresses her mother had sewn from recycled bed sheets. The sheets were dyed with the bright colours sought after by Kazakh women. Masha became an adept salesgirl. She learnt to haggle, to extract the highest price. At night she crept out with Lonka, her seasoned partner in crime, to steal beet from the sugar mill.

Masha's mother converted the beet into soup. When the family had eaten their fill, she would carry the soup to the boys of a Vilna yeshiva. An entire school of biblical scholars had fled to Merke. She fed the students and helped sustain them in their stubborn quest for redemption. Surely, the Messiah was finally on the way, argued the scholars. Their people had become wanderers yet again. The yeshiva boys had resurrected their gilded arks and Torah scrolls in the mudbrick shelters of Merke, where they clung to their one constant, their one true home: their trusted scriptures and obstinate love of a tribal God.

On summer nights Masha slept outside, under an arcing dome teeming with stars. On winter evenings she read by candlelight. Her life orbited around the village school, the epicentre of her new life. She fell in love with the Russian classics. She fed her voracious appetite for knowledge. She read so long and so late that in the mornings her father scolded her for wasting precious fuel.

For three full years the Frydmans lived in Merke; until a November night in 1944, when Masha's father failed to return home. He arrived next morning, badly bruised and ashen-faced. 'Pack immediately,' he ordered. Only when they were well on their way did he dare explain. He had been interrogated and beaten by the secret police. They had demanded he become a spy. They had left him with the devil's choice: either become an informer and pry into the lives of fellow refugees, or be transported back to the labour camps of the north.

A horse-drawn cart conveyed the family out of Merke. They

travelled within the shadows of mountains, under cover of night. They journeyed more than one hundred kilometres west, to Dzhambul: a city of mosques and winding streets, of domes and ragged markets, of monotonous days punctuated by the muezzin's sombre call, and nights permeated by uncertainty, the fear of a sudden knocking on the door.

Masha recalls little of her Dzhambul sojourn, except for the Gypsy fortune teller who beckoned to her from a lane. 'Your hands are so delicate,' she murmured. 'So white. A girl with such white hands is destined to die young.'

And she recalls a cattle train, standing on the railway tracks. The train was crowded with Chechen refugees. They had been uprooted and deported en masse. The train remained standing on the tracks for days. From its carriages came the sounds of moaning, the cries of old women, and children, begging for water to ease their thirst.

Masha had glimpsed the future. She had glimpsed the fate of millions. The sight of the fear-stricken faces lingered on in her dreams of ghost trains crowded with disembodied white hands, reaching out from behind iron bars; and of a Gypsy fortune teller whispering, 'You will not live long. A girl with such delicate white hands is destined to die young.'

IV

The de facto Jewish parliament is assembling on the pavement outside Scheherazade, as it does every Sunday morning. In pairs, in groups of four or more, they lean on posts, against the parked cars, or prop themselves by the cafe door. While others stand, just so, like birds momentarily arrested mid-flight.

Listen to them argue. Idle by for an hour or two. Observe the hands and the arms. See them make circles and arcs. Theirs is a parliament of self-appointed ministers and speechwriters. There are many problems to be solved. One group analyses the money markets. A second argues over the fluctuating fortunes of rival political parties. A third group tears apart the weekend headlines. They pass judgment on countries near and far. They cast their eyes back to events long past. Their collective gaze extends from the first year of the twentieth century to the last.

Amidst this babble can be heard the voice of Laizer Bialer: 'So, you think you can save the world, you hero in underpants. So you think you know it all, you no-good bastard, you clever little philosopher, you fool.'

Yet when we sit alone, at a table inside the cafe, on this Sunday morning in late spring, the aggressive banter gives way to a haunting intensity. It can be seen in the eyes. They turn inwards, away from me. Laizer loses all sense of his surroundings; and, without warning, he has glided into another world.

It can come upon him any time, anywhere. He may be walking on the beach, on his daily stroll, aware of the traffic whispering on the foreshore, the waves nibbling at his feet. But Laizer is moving in his parallel universe: standing waist-deep in water beneath the arctic wilderness, or lying on his back, on the boards of a cattle truck, his body registering every bump and jolt.

Or he is being led along a dark passageway, handcuffed, driven by prison guards to a door. The same door night after night. The guards hurl him inside, and he is standing in front of an interrogator whose face is barely visible behind a single globe.

The globe moves back and forth, back and forth. Laizer is mesmerised by the swaying light; his interrogator is demanding: 'Confess! Admit that you are a foreign imperialist! An enemy alien. A spy!' The lamp is swinging back and forth, and all Laizer can see is the glaring light, and all he can hear is the monotonous drip of a tap, an endless dripping, an endless swinging back and forth.

Again the waves are swirling about his feet; Laizer is back on the cusp of the bay. He makes his way along the well-worn route. Crosses The Esplanade to Shakespeare Grove. Turns right into Acland Street. Rejoins the 'parliament', the bustling crowds, the arguments which rage on the narrow footpath; and he enters Scheherazade, eager to see a familiar face, to find a table surrounded by friends, even if they are a bunch of no-good bastards!

This morning, however, we are seated alone, as prearranged, so that Laizer can recount his tale. 'I cannot see any continuity in my journey,' he murmurs. 'Only broken lines.'

Laizer tells his story in fragments, and in the telling he moves from anxiety to light-heartedness, from obsession to banter, from one city to another. It is left to me to reconstruct the map and the chronology. A scribe, a no-good scribbler, I cannot turn back. What had begun as a simple newspaper story has exploded beyond my grasp. I listen. And I record. Driven by the knowledge that the old men are moving on, nearing the ends of their tumultuous lives; driven by a sense that it would be a tragic betrayal if their stories disappeared without trace.

In the final months of 1939 Laizer decided to forsake Wolfke's, and the interminable discussions of what to do, where to go, where to seek refuge; the debates that raged in the saloon, the restaurant and smoke-filled banquet hall:

'Vilna is safe,' argued one.

'Vilna is too close to the front line,' asserted another.

'Perhaps it is better to run for the east,' reckoned a third.

'Better the devil one knows,' reasoned others.

'Perhaps we should run to the north,' interjected the realists. 'To the Baltic Sea. Scandinavia. Or perhaps the Atlantic coast.'

'And fall into the Nazi trap?'

Until Laizer had heard enough. The indecision began to suffocate him. Or perhaps it was simply on impulse that he forsook Vilna and his friends.

In February 1940, Laizer moved south from Vilna, deeper into Soviet territory, through White Russia and the Ukraine. Despite the fact that he was a refugee, he knew his Polish passport would be suspect on Soviet soil. So what? These were desperate times, and he prided himself on being a gambler. Soviet-controlled Vilna was too close to Nazi-occupied Poland for comfort. Only a fragile pact between Germany and Russia kept Hitler's armies at bay; and Laizer knew that pacts and alliances between empires could change overnight.

He was arrested by a patrol of Red Army soldiers, charged with illegal crossing of the border, and entrained, under armed guard, to a Soviet prison in the Ukrainian city of Lvov.

'There were 106 prisoners in one double room,' Laizer recalls, with precision. 'We would measure the space we allotted ourselves to sleep in. If you wanted to turn over, you had to ask the people around you to turn with you. It was never dark; all night a single light burned.

'It was a comedy. Our toilet was a drum, standing in the corner of the room. The room did stink of our own waste. We smelt like vagrants, unwashed tramps. We had a daily ration of bread and diluted soup. You could not call it soup. It tasted like swamp water. Every fortnight we received a matchbox full of sugar. This was our first great luxury. There was only one window, high up, and through it, from a certain prized position, you could see a patch of sky, a ray of sun, or dark clouds rushing by. Or, sometimes, even the moon. This was our second and final luxury.

'In return, we could be searched at any time. We were made to undress. They probed every orifice. They looked for weapons, pencils, for surplus rations of bread.

'There was a Polish priest, a fellow prisoner, who did make a chess set out of stale bread. He carved it with his bare hands. Such artistry I never saw in my life. Such elegant knights and pawns. Such fine detail. The chess set was more important to him than food.

'To stay sane, we became inventors and improvisers. When our clothes wore out we carved needles out of fish bones retrieved from our soup. We drew yarn out of our rags, threaded the yarn through the bones, and patched up our clothes.

'And always, they did come to question us late at night. I was led through a long corridor to the interrogation room. The interrogators were well dressed, well fed. I was not beaten. I was not physically tortured. They wanted just one thing, a confession. They claimed they had evidence, but they wanted me to own up to being a foreign spy. It was a kind of game; with always the same questions, always the single globe swinging back and forth, always the dripping of a tap behind me.

'Often my interrogators looked bored. At other times their posture was more threatening, their voices harsh. To this day, when I hear a tap dripping in another room, I have to stop it, immediately. My hearing is so sharp I can pick it up even when the drip, drip, drip, is very light. I am always tightening taps, replacing washers, old pipes. I want to be sure. Prevention is better than cure.

'And I must have soap, on hand, everywhere. For ten months I did not have a shower or a bath; for almost a year I lived with the stench of the unwashed; so today I keep bars of soap on every sink, in the shower recesses, in every cupboard, in every room, and I wash myself many times a day. It is a madness, I know, but I cannot help it. I cannot stand the thought of being unclean. I cannot see continuity in my journey, only broken lines.'

Towards the end of 1940, Laizer and his fellow inmates were marched from Lvov prison to the central station. They were herded into cattle wagons and conveyed north, through the Ukraine to Byelorussia. They skirted Moscow to the north-east, spent days shunted aside in carriages idling on provincial tracks, jerked forward in stops and starts, and came to a final halt, an eternity later, in Kotlas, a frontier town at the end of a north-western Russian line.

They journeyed from Kotlas by river barge, hundreds of kilometres north, to Pechora, a town perched on the western flanks of the Urals. They marched on by foot into a world of permafrost and gales. They trudged over frozen streams, across desolate plains of white, broken by an occasional tree, a solitary hut, a stunted bush. They marched as if in a trance, beyond exhaustion. Beyond dates. Beyond all reckoning.

They moved on even as Laizer fell. The snow was a soft cushion calling for surrender. It seemed to wink at him. He gave in to an imagined warmth. He felt a blessed sense of relief. He closed his eyes, sank towards oblivion, and allowed the life-force to drift away. The world was receding from his grasp.

He was about to give way when he felt a succession of sharp blows against his body. Laizer was struck in the ribs, his legs, his upper arms, and thighs. He opened his eyes and glimpsed, standing over him, his Polish comrade, a former policeman, the fellow prisoner who had become his marching partner, his closest friend. He observed his friend's fury as he kicked, and he heard his words, as if drifting in another realm: 'Get up! Get up you fool! Get up you hopeless shit!'

It took some time for Laizer to awake from his stupor, to feel the pain. As he stirred, he glimpsed the night sky. He heard the voice drifting closer. He felt the marrow seeping back into his bones. His comrade dragged him to his feet, slapped his face, gave him one last kick, and propelled him into the night.

As he stumbled on, Laizer observed an eerie light cast upon the snow. When he glanced up he saw a full moon so large and so near, it seemed he could reach out and touch it. Or eat it. Or step onto it, to wander its desolate craters and hills. It filled the skies. It filled the heavens. It filled his entire being, and, for a moment, it took him away from the smell of sweat, the life-sapping fatigue, the struggling breath.

On that night, under an impassive moon, Laizer discovered parallel universes, hovering side by side, one of beauty, one of ugliness, one permeated by darkness, the other suffused with light. On that night Laizer regained his childhood sense of naivety and awe; and he realised that by learning to manoeuvre between these alternate universes he could generate the charge of energy necessary for him to pull through. On that night, Laizer became a survivor.

Broken lines and maps. I look them up in the library, in the *Times Atlas of the World*. I search for Vorkuta, the labour camp where Laizer's long march came to an end. I turn to a map of the Arctic, the roof of the world, the point at which the lines of longitude converge to form the North Pole.

I become giddy, nauseous almost, merely by tracing the lines. From Vorkuta, latitude 68 degrees north, I move anti-clockwise, in a circle, following the line of latitude over the polar Urals, the East Siberian and Bering seas, across Alaska, via the Arctic Ocean, to a white expanse known as Greenland, and beyond it to the Barents Sea, full circle back to Vorkuta.

I have sensed the vastness. I am plotting lines that form ancestral maps, that unify fractured journeys across continents and oceans; lines that convey ancient melodies and longings, and twist and curve and break off into unexpected detours, to converge upon a cafe called Scheherazade.

I find them there, of course, when next I return. The unlikely trio. Yossel, Zalman and Laizer. Bent over their pastries and coffees. And they know what I am looking for.

'He makes a living from them, that no-good scribbler,' says Laizer.

'And why not?' says Zalman.

'Better to sell stories than *shmuttes*, recycled rags,' adds Yossel.

'You earn far more selling *shmuttes*,' I reply.

'I am not so sure of that,' says Zalman.

'And what, my philosopher friend, can anyone be sure of?' asks Laizer.

'Perhaps only stories,' says Zalman. 'The rest is speculation.'

'So, my clever little philosopher,' retorts Laizer. 'What makes you so sure about the value of stories? Most of us tell them in such a way that we look good, and others look bad. We twist everything to our advantage. We do not tell stories. We create *bobbe mayses*. Grandmothers' tales!'

'At least they help pass the time,' says the prosaic Yossel.

'So! I can see it now! I know your little tricks. You are winding up to tell us your *bobbe mayses* about your wonderful Warsaw and Krochmalna Street. You are preparing to tell us about your no-good friends Mendel Mandelbaum and Stanislaw the pimp. And how you became a hero in underpants.'

'Yossel is right,' Zalman intervenes. 'We tell stories to kill time. After all, this is how we passed the time in Wolfke's when the world was coming to an end.'

'Such pearls of wisdom, such wonderful turns of phrase, you clever little philosophers!' says Laizer. 'It was easy to be clever while you sat in Wolfke's and let time idle by. While you were waiting for the end of days, I was labouring beneath the snows of Vorkuta. And while you were travelling away from Vilna, first-class, I was pushing boulders up ice-clad hills.

'Martin, you cannot imagine it,' Laizer tells me, as Yossel and Zalman move away. 'We lived in the Arctic Circle. We lived with lice. We would bet on them for entertainment. How do you say it in English? Odds or evens. We counted them and, when we got sick of the game, we would make a fire in the barracks, take off our shirts, hold them over the flames, and watch the parasites drop off. They fell in the hundreds; and a day later they were back again.

'You cannot imagine it. In winter the earth was a solid mass, rock hard. In summer it softened. The soil was covered in red berries and moss. We were building an airfield. We moved rocks with our raw hands. Two people could barely carry them. We were like Sisyphus, lifting stones, dropping them, and watching them roll backwards. Our food rations depended upon how many rocks we moved, so like Sisyphus we retrieved them and started all over again.

'After a month or so I was sent to work in the coal mines. This was the highlight of my stay. We descended by lift, perhaps two hundred metres under the earth. We worked in complete darkness, waist-deep in ice-cold water. We froze and choked on the dust. And all I could think of was food, my daily ration of bread.

'I was obsessed with food. When I fell asleep, I dreamt of my mother's cholent and roasts, Wolfke's brisket and schnitzels, Vilna's bakeries and cafes. All the wise sayings of the philosophers were reduced to just one thought: food. We searched every corner, every obscure hole, for just one more crumb.

'We were entitled to a ration of bread, perhaps six hundred grams, that is, if you fulfilled your work quota for the day. Otherwise an amount was deducted. The bread was lousy and the bread cutters were criminals. Sometimes they would cut off a bit less so they could keep more for themselves.

'The common criminals were treated better than the political prisoners. In the gulag, political prisoners were on the lowest rung. There was a rigid class system in the classless society! On the top rung were the *nachalniks,* the camp commanders and party bosses. Then came the guards and soldiers who kept their eyes on our every move; and in the stinking barracks the criminals were the true bosses, while we were the slaves.

'The criminals controlled the kitchens. They were well-fed. They bribed the guards who let them through the barbed-wire fences into the women's camp. They fell upon the women like wild beasts. After all, they were full of energy and zest. But the rest of us had no interest in sex. When you are hungry, food is more erotic than sex. The memory of a Vilna

Sabbath stew was far more enticing than the most desirable of women.

'In our spare time we sat on our bunks and watched the criminals play cards. Mostly they did play for other people's boots or overcoats. The loser would be obliged to attack one of the political prisoners, grab his spoils and give them to the winner. On one occasion they even played for their fingers. The loser stood up, took an axe, and chopped off a finger. I did see it myself.

'This is what happens to you when you are cut off from the rest of the world. You become deranged. And we were cut off, completely. We were surrounded by barbed wire. Every hundred metres or so there stood a guard tower. If you tried to escape you were shot. And if you got away, where was there to run? The nearest railway line was five hundred kilometres away. The only way out was the way we had come in, by river barge and on foot. Otherwise, the only certain exit was a grave, dug deep in the Arctic earth.

'We did live in a world of our own. There were Tartars and Uzbeks, Poles and Jews. There were Russians, Mongolians, Chinese and Africans, Gypsies and Armenians. And we got on quite well, mind you. We were in the same black hole together. Within weeks of our arrival, we all looked the same. We were dressed in the same rags. Our shoes were held together with wire. We were covered in sores. Our eyes were red, our faces unshaven. We were a mess of skin and protruding bones. At night many of us did stagger around with 'chicken blindness', brought on by lack of food. And we smelt the same, of stale sweat and lice-infested rags.

'We belonged to the same big, hopeless family. We were a brotherhood of no-good bastards, a nation of fools trapped on the roof of the world.'

Some dates remain indelibly carved in the mind. On 13 October 1941, Laizer Bialer and his fellow prisoners, those who had once been Polish citizens, stood in the assembly yard of their labour camp within the Arctic Circle. The brief 'summer' was long over, the polar cap was girdled in snow, the north winds were about to descend, and the prisoners were told they were about to be freed.

As he stood in the assembled crowd, Laizer was struck by the thought: what an odd word freedom is. Free to do what? To go where? Thousands of kilometres south-west stood the city of his loved ones, of his youth. He had not heard from them for two years. And somewhere in that vastness called the Soviet Union there were former comrades who, like Laizer, had disappeared on the trek east, in flight from the same inferno that had driven them from their homes.

Yes, he was free. And alone. The thought appealed to him in a curious way. To be alone was to feel light, to be stripped back to essentials, to a bare mattress in a three-tiered bunk, to his wired shoes and the rags on his back. But, at the same time, it brought back an almost forgotten ache, an ache he had suppressed in order to survive an exile that seemed to have no end. This is what was so curious about freedom. It seemed so fragile.

The long descent began. The former prisoners were given a ration of food and put on board a barge that conveyed them through waters that had not quite frozen over. Along the Vorkuta River they drifted, through erratic currents and congregations of ice. The land about them retreated against the encroaching darkness. Mist-filled days became extended twilights which were engulfed by expanding nights.

Into the Pechora River the barge sailed, its bunks crowded with a cargo of freed slaves who had learnt, in the years of their imprisonment, to take each day as the first; who had come to realise it does not pay to get carried away by brittle hopes. They were not surprised, therefore, when the barge master, fearing for his safety upon a river that was freezing over, guided his boat to the banks and ordered the passengers off.

The band of castaways set out on a trek along the banks of the Pechora. In the days that followed, as their food supplies dwindled, and the cold took hold, there were those who fell by the way; and what Laizer recalls, above all, was the expression on their faces as they finally surrendered and gave way to the snow. Their eyes closed upon a smile that seemed to say: our journey has ended; we are out of this *gehennim*, but you, my dear comrade, you who still cling to life, who seem to think that there is an end to this madness, you must go on.

The ranks thinned. The larger band broke up into gangs. The

gangs roved the countryside. They rested during the dwindling hours of daylight, and moved on under the cover of night. They raided villages and farms. They stole food at knifepoint. They dug potatoes out of the cold earth. They swallowed snow to appease their hunger and thirst. And when, at last, they reached the railway tracks, they leapt aboard moving trains to steal supplies, and jumped off at the outskirts of kolkhozes, where they scoured the fields for the final remains of the autumn harvest.

'I cannot see continuity in my journey,' repeats Laizer. 'Only broken lines.' We sit with our coffees in Scheherazade and we work in tandem to rejoin them. Laizer recalls a sojourn in Sverdlovsk, a city in the central Urals, and a temporary job in a power station. He recalls days lived in a torpor, weeks during which he drifted, months on end when he merely existed.

In the spring of 1942, Laizer was drafted into the Red Army. After a brief training period he was ordered to assemble with his unit at the Sverdlovsk station. One minute before they were about to depart for the front he was ordered out of his carriage. As he stood on the platform Laizer was divested of his rifle, his bayonet, his ammunition, and handed back his civilian clothing. As a Polish citizen and former prisoner he had been judged untrustworthy to take on the duties of a soldier.

Laizer was assigned to a work battalion and dispatched by train in the opposite direction, towards the town of Serov. Again he journeyed north, three hundred kilometres through the Urals, the hinterlands of an empire at war. The tracks hummed through the dark, past remote hamlets and streams, past shadowy forests and fields, over mountain passes and bridges scaling ravines.

The train moved by stations at which troops were assembling to be transported to the front. At one station Laizer glimpsed the injured en route home from the battlefields. He saw the bandaged limbs of amputees, the vacant eyes of those who had barely escaped with their lives. He sensed their anguish. He heard their collective cry, which vanished back into the darkness, reduced to snatches of conversation, the moans of disturbed dreamers, the mutterings of the sleepless.

The labourers of the work battalions lay in the crowded carriages, their bodies curled in upon themselves, as if in retreat from reality. They conjured the warmth of imaginary wombs, and relished their rare moments of respite, when constant movement and fatigue conspired to still even the most feverish minds. And Laizer realised that what he had mistaken for silence was, in fact, the crooning of the tracks, forever arcing towards an abyss; tracks which rocked and cradled the dispossessed, and evoked childhood ditties and lullabies; tracks which reverberated with the elusive voice of a mother singing:

> Oh come now, quiet evening,
> And rock the fields to sleep,
> I sing you a song of praise,
> Oh silent evening of mine.

How still it has become,
The night has finally come,
The little white birch tree,
Remains wrapped in darkness, alone.

February in Melbourne can be the wildest month. A hot northerly wind is gusting. It raises dust from the pavements, and whips sand across the foreshore. It caps swirling wavelets with foam, and spins buoys, yellow and red, into twirling tops. It lifts late summer leaves and pine needles from the gutters. It upturns outdoor tables and chairs, and hurls beach umbrellas from their moorings.

A gang of teenage boys huddle about their ghetto-blasters on a strip of grass above the foreshore. A cormorant struggles to stay aloft. Bathers lie spreadeagled in the shallows. An addict, lost in a heroin fix, dances beneath a palm, while her partner sways in her shadow, a beer can in each hand.

And Laizer walks the usual route, from his St Kilda flat to the cafe. His face is flushed. His nerves are frayed. The upper buttons on his shirt are undone. His shock of thinning white chest-hair bristles in the wind.

He moves from the foreshore beyond The Esplanade, to Shakespeare Grove; rounds the corner into Acland Street. He approaches the two palms, on either side of the road, recently planted, fully grown. They are two sentinels, keeping guard, he remarks to himself, aloud. He has almost reached his goal. The neon oasis is drawing him on. He is running as he bursts through Scheherazade's doors.

'You see, Martin, you no-good scribbler?' he says, breathless, as he sits down beside me. 'Listen to those winds. Even here, in the golden land, we are just a breath away from chaos.'

Laizer is nervous. He cannot sit still. He stands up, paces about, returns to his seat. It will take time for him to settle down. I know the pattern well, his approach and retreat, his desire to withdraw, his conflicting need to tell. But today, more than a month since I last saw him, the contrasts are harsher than usual. The north winds are on the prowl. They are our *sirocco*. Our *hamsin*. The closest our city possesses to a desert wind.

The airconditioner hums. The cool has set in. Laizer's nerves are settling. He is calm enough to sit still; and to smile. Laizer is as warm as the north winds, but far more generous. Once a friend, he will remain a friend. A *khaver*. A loyal companion. After all, I have accompanied him on quite a journey now and, for this moment, at least, we are both no-good bastards taking shelter from the same winds.

Laizer describes northerly winds of a far different kind. They whirled like dervishes, in savage tornadoes of snow. They hurled hailstones into the eyes, and gnawed at the nerves with ice. 'Martin, you are a writer, but words cannot capture it. It is impossible. You feel nature lashing you, laughing at you. You become a nothing. Your body is a mere bag of bones.'

Laizer recalls it as a time of taunting beauty, the twenty months he worked on the ancient trading route called the Vizir.

For over a century the route had snaked, twenty metres wide, through the forests of western Siberia, hundreds of kilometres east, from Serov to Tobolsk.

In summer the path was submerged in impassable bogs and swamps, littered with fallen trees and encroaching forest. Russian merchants travelled the Vizir in winter. Horse-drawn sleds conveyed their merchandise in search of 'the easterners', hunting tribes of the taiga who exchanged furs for axes and ammunition, animal skins for vodka and tobacco. The sleds returned with the raw coats of arctic reindeer and silver foxes, polar bears and Siberian tigers.

Laizer delights in this history. The terrain was so difficult that the route was broken every thirty kilometres by stations where the merchants obtained fresh supplies and horses. Over time, the stations became hamlets. Each hamlet expanded into networks of extended families. When the children intermarried it was the custom for the woman to live in her husband's hamlet. The hamlets grew into villages that bore the name of the principal family. After the revolution the villages had become kolkhozes, co-operatives that retained the family name; and life continued, as it had, for many generations.

For those twenty months, Laizer moved east along the trading route with his work battalion, constructing towers for the Red Army. The towers were to be used to survey the terrain and determine the impacts of climatic change. There were fourteen workers in all: Russians and Ukrainians, Gypsies and Chechens, an Ingush and an Armenian; a disparate band welded by fate into a close-knit gang of frontier men.

They built makeshift roads. They dragged sleds weighed down with equipment through mosquito-infested swamps. They covered the swamps with logs to ease the way. They axed the timber into precise lengths, ready to assemble into the towers' pyramidal shape. They cut down ageing trees with which they built shelters over the ice. They slept on branches of silver birch. They spread layers of soil and moss for insulation. A permanent fire burnt at the entrance. In summer the fire smoked out mosquitoes; and in winter it provided warmth and inspired stories.

What else was there to do on long winter nights when the sun set within hours of rising? The labourers exchanged tales by a fire accompanied by the wailing of a wolf, the hoot of an owl, a sudden gust of wind. They talked about their years in prison camps, their children, wives, lovers and squandered lives. They were the heirs of a revolution that had promised so much, yet delivered so little. They had once imagined future riches, but now they lived for each passing day.

Yet there were moments which caught them unawares, and overpowered them with their beauty. More than half a century later Laizer was to recall such a moment with hallucinatory clarity.

At dawn, on a winter's day, while on the way to work, he had come across a village suspended from the sky. Snow had fallen through a breezeless night. It clung to the eyebrows and eyelashes, to his beard and rotting gloves. It contoured the trees, the cottage chimneys, the village wells and angled roofs. It engulfed every protrusion: a solitary nail, a leaning shovel, an abandoned broom.

Frozen particles floated about him, alight against a crimson sun. A strand of smoke rose from each chimney, pencil-thin, into a rouged mist. And, on these glowing strands, the village seemed to hang between the reddened sky and snow-clad earth.

Laizer knew it was an illusion, but he felt elated nevertheless. He could hear the faint song of creation, or so he allowed himself to believe. This is how things really are, it seemed to murmur. This is the perfection that underlies the chaos. This is what lies beyond the veil of suffering, beyond the betrayal you call life.

The melody ceased. The sun broke through. The village sank back into the white. Laizer stood for a moment longer, reluctant to let go; and was overcome by a profound sadness. He looked down at his ragged clothes; and felt the pangs of hunger returning, the frost flowing back into his bones.

The beauty of that image could not save him. It could not take away the pain of longing, or restore him to his loved ones. The contrast was cruel: so much beauty set against the reality of his enslavement. The universe was, after all, detached. It had lifted him so high, only to cast him back into the cold; and there was no lasting support that could cushion the fall.

Laizer turned and resumed his reluctant journey, through

the forests, back to his work brigade, to another day of labour in a Siberian glade.

Laizer wipes the perspiration from his brow. He finishes his coffee, and orders another. He stirs in a teaspoon of sugar. A second. And a third. His forehead is creased in concentration. On his face there is a childlike smile, a look of wonder. He is looking downwards, at his hands, which are spread before him on the table. He is gripped by the rotation of northern skies, and the turning of seasons long past.

In spring the rivers broke loose. Rafts of ice, uprooted trees, dismembered branches, careered downstream. The conifers oozed resinous ambers and blood reds. The scent of the sap was intoxicating. Like a darkroom print coming into focus, the earth emerged in full colour. Quilts of leaves shook free from melting snows. Crimson berries that had lain beneath the snow all winter appeared underfoot, radiant against a translucent white.

Days earlier the workers had separated into two bands at the banks of a stream. Laizer had moved on with an advance party to build the huts, and prepare the way. They waded through swamps and marshes. Water soaked their bark-plaited shoes. A week later, in heavy rains, they ran out of rations. They retraced their way to the stream and, as they drew near, they saw it had broken its banks. The stream was now a kilometre in width.

The work party lashed some logs together. They launched

their primitive craft upon the river and guided it with wooden poles. Just as they were about to touch the other side, the raft crashed into an uprooted tree borne downstream by the accelerating currents.

The raft capsized. When Laizer rose to the water's surface he glimpsed a log floating by. He grabbed it, sank his axe into the log and used it as a hook to lever himself out of the swirling currents. His companions, who had swum ashore, ran along the embankment shouting instructions. When he came within reach they grabbed the log and dragged Laizer back onto solid earth.

Yes, it was a time of taunting beauty, those twenty months upon the Vizir. Each season had its allure, and its dangers. The summers were all the more glorious for being brief. The sun barely sank below the horizon before it rose again into a sky that had retained its glow. It was then that the flowers appeared, their fleeting lives compensated for by the intensity of their colour and fragrance. But, again, the beauty mocked them; summer was the season of plagues and hard labour. Mobs of mosquitoes swarmed about them as Laizer and his companions made up for lost time.

Seventeen hours a day they slaved on the towers, assembling each floor with infinite care, storey by storey, from its ten-metre base, to a sixth-level summit, two metres square; and in their rare spare moments, to appease their hunger, they trapped rabbits and arctic foxes; and reeled in fish and water fowl.

They also feasted on the *glukhar*, a large bird that they prized for its ample flesh, and the ease with which it could be trapped, because it was believed to be deaf. They cleaned the bird and discarded the entrails at the periphery of the camp. Just after sunrise a member of the brigade stepped out of his hut into the path of a bear. It had been lured into the camp by the scent of the bird's remains. The worker ran back to the hut to rouse his companions.

'Grab pots and pans. Grab whatever you can,' advised the more experienced forest workers. They ran out screaming, pounding their makeshift drums. They stamped their feet on the ground. They waved their arms like windmills caught in a gale. The bear raised its head and lumbered away. This is what struck Laizer, the bear's composure. It did not run. It merely turned and strolled away.

Just as unobtrusively, summer gave way to autumn. Mush-rooms littered the earth. The undergrowth was a mess of lichens and rotting leaves. Laizer inhaled the cool aroma of damp foliage and decay. But there was little time to savour it. Ice-edged winds were a reminder, the forward scouts of impending gloom. The first frosts spread their veils over the forest floor. Laizer and his companions worked against time.

Their most important autumn task was to fell trees, the keys to their survival. They provided fuel, timber for their log huts, and the building blocks for the towers. The men worked in pairs upon each tree, eight men to four trees. The first snows had begun to fall. Three of the trees tumbled towards the river over an incline, as planned. The fourth remained standing.

Laizer approached it, struck an axe into the split, and levered the gap as he had been taught to do. His partner, a Ukrainian, stood behind him grasping a pole, at the ready, to push the tree on its way.

Instead of falling towards the river the tree slipped off its cut and toppled backwards; at first slowly, mesmerising its assailants with its deceptive speed. Laizer was struck in the chest. His partner received a direct blow to the head and was instantly killed. Laizer was saved by the snow that cushioned his fall. He lay in bed for eight days, unable to move, and emerged condemned to feel the pain, every day, for the rest of his life.

As for their second winter, it was the time to take stock. To hibernate, and prepare for the return of the light. When the night was clear the brigade worked by the glow of the moon. Frost clung to their faces. Each breath was bloated with snow. Perspiration turned to ice. They laboured in silence, broken only by a snatch of song, an anecdote. Or they discussed the exploits of their most loved workmate, Dobynda the Gypsy.

'We all loved him, that no-good bastard. He was not afraid. He spoke the truth in his half-smiling and half-cynical way. He knew how to control his laughter, when he had to. It was the laughter of a man with lizards in his guts. When our overseers hurled mud at him, it would never stick. Nothing could touch him. He did float through each day without a care.

'"Hey Dobynda, you are idling; work harder," the foreman once warned.

'"Why should I work harder," Dobynda replied, "when you measure the soil with spades and the food with spoons? Now, if you would measure the food with spades and the soil with spoons, then I'd work faster than the devil."'

Laizer laughs. Sips his coffee. Stirs in another sugar.

'Because of Dobynda I once ate more food in a day than I would eat for an entire month. He awoke me late at night. "Come," he said. "It is Easter. Christ is rising. I can tell by the size of the moon. We should take advantage of his resurrection, his rebirth."

'We did steal out and make our way to the nearest village, fifteen kilometres away, by the light of the rising moon. We reached the village in the early morning. We knocked on every door and repeated the magic words: *Christos Voskres.* Christ has risen. And each villager, no matter how poor, gave us some food— a slice of black bread, a potato, a cucumber, a hard-boiled egg.

'We left the village with our sacks full. We sat in the forest and filled our bellies until they ached. Never were two atheists so grateful for the rising of Christ as we were on that Easter day.'

Laizer lapses into silence. The smile fades. His eyes are drained. The spell has broken. We are the last two diners left in the cafe. Our plates are strewn with crumpled napkins, our coffee cups down to the dregs. The tables are littered with ashtrays full of blackened butts. The night manager is checking the books, the waitresses are stacking the chairs, dimming the lights.

'*Genug.* Enough of these grandmother's tales,' quips Laizer. 'Besides, you no-good bastard, you idle scribbler, you should have enough stories now for an entire encyclopaedia of the world's follies and woes.'

Laizer has come to know this fragment of bayside suburb well. He has lived here longer now than any other place he has ever been; and its lack of symmetry suits him. The streets do not run to a simple grid. The sea does not allow it. The foreshore bends to the bay. The Esplanade curves with the coastline. The thoroughfares are interwoven like lace.

The sea has darned the lace; pulled it into its natural shapes. Only later did the town-planners come and impose their own more rigid order as best they could. They followed the contours of their minds' eyes, which were guided by the cities of their youth. Later still came the new immigrants, from all corners of the earth. They recreated their remembrances, their cravings, their Scheherazades.

Yet Laizer walks these streets as if they do not exist. He moves in and out of his parallel universes, pursued by the whispers of obstinate ghosts. He wanders a world of mirages. He walks the tracks of Siberia.

When Laizer and I next meet, at the appointed hour, I sense a new urgency. It can be heard in the tone of his voice, in the way he fumbles for words. It can be detected in the way he clasps his elbows, winds his arms about himself, or lifts them up in a hopeless gesture. I feel the limits of my craft, the limits of what words can convey; and I am driven by an urge to enter into Laizer's parallel worlds with him, hand-in-hand; to burst beyond the walls of the cafe, beyond the streets of St Kilda, into the images he is trying to create.

'Words cannot describe those months on the tracks of Siberia,' Laizer says. 'We did live in a world without an end. The paths wound their way into infinity. I was a nothing in an indifferent machine.

'That is the word I am looking for: *indifference*. This is what was so brutal about Siberia, the prison in Lvov, those wasted years in Vorkuta. This is what was so cruel about every *nachalnik*, every camp commandant, party boss, or interrogator I faced: their indifference. And their contempt. They did not put any value on your life.

'Do you know what this means, when no one cares? When no one knows who you are? When there is no longer any warmth?

'There were times when I was overcome by a panic, by the thought that here, in this wilderness, I would perish; and my tales would perish with me. I would be buried in an unmarked grave. No one would ever know what I had gone through. Martin, I have not yet begun to tell my story, and the stories of my workmates. Of the Ukrainian who died beside me as the tree fell. He had been sentenced to fifteen years of hard labour because he refused to give up the milk of his last cow to the party. He insisted on keeping it to feed his own family.

'When his wife discovered he had been shifted from the labour camps to a work brigade, she was overjoyed. She saw it as the first sign of his return. She thought that perhaps, soon, after so many years, he would be released, and allowed to journey home. Her letter, full of optimism, arrived the day after her husband was killed.

'We treasured that letter. It became our common property. We did read it, aloud, over and again. We paused at each line, and argued over its meaning. We debated whether she had loved her husband or not. Sometimes we were convinced she had betrayed him. At other times we were certain that hers were a lover's words. We did adopt her as our own. She became our imaginary partner, a reminder of our warped fate.

'Each one of my workmates had a similar tale: the Chechen, the Russian, the Ingush, the Armenian. Each one had been sentenced to years of hard labour for a triviality. And each one had to learn to accept his cruel lot. Dobynda the Gypsy expressed it best. He would laugh, point to the heavens, and exclaim: "If you believe that you will find a way out of this shit, you may as well go beat your head against the sky!"

'Yet there were other times, as I trudged from one hour to the next, when I believed that one day I *would* prevail, that one day I *would* tell my unbelievable tales. I imagined that I would bring back a deeper truth about the taunting beauty of nature. I would bring back my experience of human indifference, and expose the system that produced it. I imagined the astonished faces of the friends and family I had left behind, how they would hang on every detail, on each measured word. I did lie awake at night, beside my snoring workmates, and conjure the picture of my triumphant return. I saw myself walking the final steps to the door. I would tell my story, and my life would not have been wasted.

'Perhaps only a poet can truly describe it. A poet who has been there, and has gone through it himself. A poet can say it all in just a few lines. "On the Tracks of Siberia" is the perfect poem. My poem. Written by a like mind. A parallel mind. By a man who once walked the same roads and forest trails.'

H. Leivik was the name of the poet, of Laizer's muse. After half a lifetime of suffering, Leivik had finally found his way to the Americas, to a new life; and for a while his verse flowed freely. For a time he sang the song of his former exile and toil. But five years before he died Leivik was felled by a stroke. He could no longer walk, or move his arms. Or even talk, though he longed to impart the remainder of his tale.

This is how he had ended, spreadeagled upon a bed, with nurses to guide his every move. He lay in a sanatorium ward, just another voiceless patient. How could they know he had once walked the forest tracks of Siberia?

'Survival is, after all, a matter of *mazel*, of luck,' Laizer mutters. 'Of whether you hid under the bush that wasn't bombed, whether you were spared a terminal disease. Or whether you fled north or south, east or west. Leivik understood this all too well.'

And he recites the poem on this Sunday morning in

Scheherazade. In Yiddish. The mother tongue. He recites it amidst the clamour of voices, the clash of cutlery, the rising noise:

'Even now
on the tracks of Siberia
you can find
a button,
a frayed shoelace of mine,
a belt,
a fragment of clay cup,
a page from a sacred book.
Even now
in the streams of Siberia
you can find
some trace:
a sliver of submerged raft;
in the forests
a bloodied rag dried stiff;
on the snow, frozen footprints petering out.'

On a winter morning in 1944, Laizer awoke in the workers' camp to find his legs swollen from the cold, after days of wading through snow. His legs were bloated boils, oozing pus and blood. He made his way, on skis, thirty kilometres distant, to the nearest village.

The doctor ignored the boils. He placed a thermometer

under Laizer's arm. Because he was not running a temperature the doctor could not provide him with an exemption from work. He had no choice, he insisted. Those were the regulations and, in the Soviet empire, arbitrary regulations counted above all.

Laizer returned to the camp the following afternoon, and he was charged by Red Army officers with having deserted his battalion. His work companions chided him for not flicking the thermometer with his hands to raise the temperature. He was still an innocent, they told him. They knew they would never see him again. For this is how it always ended.

Yet there were tears in their eyes as Laizer was escorted from the camp. He had been a loyal companion. They admired him for his youthful energy, his good humour, his hard work. Their tears evoked memories of red embers glowing on white nights, and of star-filled galaxies vaulting over winter fires.

A horse-drawn sled conveyed Laizer from the Vizir to a military camp where he was sentenced to six months in prison; and it was in prison that the dream took hold, the same dream, night after night.

It is a Friday night, the Sabbath eve. Laizer is wandering the streets of Vilna. The streets curve in upon each other. He moves over the cobbled lanes of the old quarters. He is lost in a circular maze. He catches glimpses of loved ones. Like mirages, the figures evaporate, until one remains, his father.

He escorts Laizer to the ground-floor apartment that was the family home. He moves like an automaton. He is beyond intimate reach. He leads his son down a flight of stairs to a large cellar.

In the cellar stands the table at which they sat together, as a family, for their meals; the table at which they had broken bread and welcomed the Sabbath bride; at which Laizer's mother had lit and blessed the candles and served the Sabbath meal.

The table is covered in a white cloth. The whiteness is heightened by flickering shadows in the semi-dark. Laizer's father sits with his hands under his chin. He stares at the five candles glued to the white cloth. The wax has dripped into mounds that rise by each candle's side. Only one remains alight.

'Why only one?' Laizer asks. 'Where is mother? Where is my brother, Heniek? Where is my sister, Khannah?'

Laizer's father cannot answer. He has slumped forwards. He no longer moves. His face is gone. Laizer searches for the familiar details. For the look of merriment that once encircled his father's eyes; the knowing smile that had comforted him as a child; but all that remains is the elusive silhouette of an old man, his head resting upon the table, buried in his arms.

It was only much later, when he returned to the city of rubble that had once been his home, that Laizer came to know: his father and mother, his sister and brother, perished, in a furnace of gas, at about the time when he first dreamed his recurring dream. He remained the one survivor of an entire family.

V

Zalman clings to the sea. He walks to his familiar markers. He ascends the shallow peak of Ormond Hill. In the distance, he can just make out the mountains of the Great Divide; it rises above the flat hinterland, an ancient presence, barely visible on this autumn day. It takes his breath away, this expansive view of the bay; and, as always, when he descends he feels weightless.

Zalman strides against the southerly wind; it is a scorpion wind. It penetrates the marrow and enflames the eyes. He notes the full tide. The waters surge onto the rocks. The spray leaps over the retaining wall. He skirts the yachting marina, veers back towards the lighthouse, and regains the shore. He scans the full sweep of the bay, from the marina to St Kilda pier. Beyond it rises the inner city, a huddle of office towers looming over a basalt plain.

It is a daily ritual, this walk, a means of regaining the feet, of restoring the present. And there are days of silver and white, of frost and muted light, on which Zalman can sense, acutely, that he lives in a city of the south.

He sits on the beach with his back to the bluestone retaining wall, and gazes at the waters of the bay. The sky hangs low, lidded with clouds. Occasionally the sun forces its way through the grey, forging a gap of transparent blue. As the sun moves back out of sight, the day is restored to pastel shades. The horizon is a faint grey line. Sky and sea are one continuum of light; and the imagination takes flight.

On the wings of a seabird Zalman glides towards the south. Over desolate islands he swoops; over rockeries teeming with hooded gannets and Pacific gulls; across stony outcrops littered with penguins and seals; over southern whales heaving their bulk through glacial waves.

He is moving towards the Antarctic, the great southern bight. He is curving towards the white-domed apex of the globe. He hears the shriek of a tern, and the drone of traffic on The Esplanade. And he is back by the retaining wall, on the city's edge, perched on its southern fringe.

Zalman savours the moment. He inhales the aroma of sea air, feels the cool texture of damp sand, and allows his back to sink into his rolled-up jacket, his makeshift pillow against the blue-stone wall.

'Such moments are the key,' he tells me in the cafe. 'At such times I always marvel that it is possible for me to feel so much at ease. In such moments all journeys come to a blessed end.'

We meet mid-week, in the afternoons. The quiet hours. When Scheherazade is almost deserted. When old men doze at their newspapers, and waitresses lean on their elbows to stare at passers-by, the Acland Street regulars, the down-at-heel and out-of-work.

It was Zalman who asked for these mid-week meetings. 'I can only talk one to one. I need quiet in which to remember, to probe beneath the surface of things. When there are too many people around me, I become an observer. I enjoy the company for company's sake, but I have no interest in joining in. I have never been a good shouter.'

Zalman speaks softly, weighing each thought, each word. As if no sentence is worth uttering unless it reveals a deeper truth; as if he is in search of lost meanings, a fractured ideal, an elusive thread.

'Martin, we were all trapped,' he says. 'What choice did we have? We had to rely on the decisions of others, on those who controlled our lives. Each day the news was more alarming. We sat in Wolfke's and waited, clinging to rumours. We sat in Wolfke's and watched the world spiral towards evil.

'It was a time when those who committed evil flourished and, once set in motion, evil begets evil. Yet amidst this evil there arose a rare saviour, like a flower emerging out of garbage.

'His name was Chiune Sugihara. He was a Japanese consul, based in the city of Kovno, 150 kilometres west of Vilna. He was willing to stamp our visas with permits that would enable us to buy our way out. So it was said. We could not believe that someone would be prepared to do such a thing, especially at that time. It was a complex procedure, full of danger. But it gave us a slim chance, a way out of our netherworld.'

Zalman pauses. Sips his black coffee. He relishes each drop. 'In every darkness there is a spark. This is what the sages have always maintained,' he says. 'And in the Lithuanian city of Kovno a young yeshiva student called Nathan Gutwirth was driven by desperation to find such a spark.'

Zalman knows the tale well. He has researched the details in his retirement years. Born in Belgium, raised in Holland, armed with a Dutch passport, Gutwirth had become aware of the extent of Nazi brutality from the final letters of his mother. She had witnessed the German occupation of Holland. 'Do not return home,' she warned her son. 'Find a way to escape.'

At the outset of July 1940, Nathan wrote to the nearest Dutch ambassador, who was stationed in Riga. Could he authorise an entry permit for Curaçao, a Dutch colony in the Caribbean Sea? Nathan had heard that a visa was not necessary for Curaçao. In subsequent correspondence, the ambassador agreed to instruct every Dutch consul in Lithuania to stamp the identity papers of any refugee, regardless of nationality.

The honorary Dutch consul in Kovno provided Gutwirth with the desired stamp: 'No Visa to Curaçao Required', it proclaimed. This was the first step. But how to get out of Vilna? And how to get out of that empire called the Soviet Union?

The least dangerous escape route was via the east. Gutwirth approached Chiune Sugihara. The consul thought it odd that no visa was required for Curaçao, but he stamped the passport, nevertheless, with a visa that allowed Gutwirth a three-week stay in Japan while in transit between any two countries.

This news spread on the refugee grapevine, via the soup

kitchens and coffee shops, boarding houses and synagogue courtyards, the crowded apartments and communal halls, the many random spaces into which those who had fled Hitler's armies were crammed.

Zalman Grintraum was among the many hopefuls who travelled from Vilna to Kovno in search of a way out. After they obtained the stamp, 'No Visa to Curaçao Required', from the Dutch consul, they gathered at the gates of Sugihara's residence. And years later, in a cafe on the opposite side of the globe, Zalman was to tell me that what struck him most about that August morning in 1940 was the silence.

It was a silence that seems to envelop consulates the world over, signifying order, legal procedures, civilised dealings. And for those who stood that morning by the consulate gates, it was also the silence of the desperate, imbued by a longing that was obvious to the Japanese consul as he gazed at the crowd from the window of an upper floor.

Sugihara had sent cables to Tokyo asking permission to issue transit visas for Japan. The replies were ambiguous. He was cautioned, advised to exercise restraint. It is said that he was finally swayed by the words of a Samurai maxim: 'Even a hunter cannot kill a bird that flies to him for refuge.'

At great personal risk, for he could have faced execution for such an act, Sugihara opened his heart to those who clamoured for assistance. Zalman was one of many who filed from the footpath, through the wrought-iron gates, up the small flight of steps that led to the consulate door. Sugihara did not even look up at him when he finally reached his desk. He was too busy applying the stamps.

Over a period of weeks, until the Kovno consulate was closed at the end of August, Sugihara issued thousands of visas. Two assistants sat in the corridor to help him cope with the demand. Even as he left the consulate for the final time bound for the Kovno railway station, he continued to stamp the visas of frantic refugees.

They pursued him through the streets. They gathered about him at the station. They followed him onto the platform. They clustered at the windows of his carriage. They ran beside it as the train began to move away; and all the while Sugihara stamped their outstretched papers; all the while he responded to their pleas.

He had followed his conscience. He had honoured the ancient maxim. He had done all he could. It would cost him dearly in terms of career, and it would take many years before he would finally receive the honour that was his due, as someone who had dared to shine a light in the falling darkness.

Zalman left Vilna on 8 February 1941. The city was covered in snow. The skies were clear, the sun's rays unimpeded. He left his room at noon, and travelled to the Vilna station by sleigh. The 'Sugihara Jews' departed at two in the afternoon. They travelled in a carriage reserved especially for them.

As the train moved through the Lithuanian countryside,

Zalman recalled the moment, two months earlier, when he had entered the Vilna offices of the NKVD. His fate rested in their hands. He risked being deported to labour camps for daring to ask for an exit permit, but he had little choice. Otherwise Sugihara's stamp would be worthless. He needed to find a way out of Russia to Japan.

Zalman was questioned at length. The room was bare, except for a desk, two chairs, and a photo of Joseph Stalin. Weeks later Zalman joined the anxious crowd at the notice wall outside the Vilna Intourist bureau. When he finally saw his name on the lists of those who had been granted an exit permit, Zalman was elated.

As soon as one battle ended, the next began. The Soviet authorities demanded that the train tickets be purchased in American dollars. Zalman's ticket was finally paid for in currency sent by relief organisations in the USA. There had been many times, in the previous fifteen months, when he felt he was trapped in a rat's maze. Only now that he was moving east did he feel free. At least, for the moment.

The train stopped in Minsk late at night. The carriage was disconnected. Zalman fell asleep, and when he awoke he found he was on the move again. He arrived in Moscow that afternoon and passed the time riding the subway. He marvelled at stations carved in marble, and at underground platforms adorned with chandeliers. He marvelled at the tiled walkways, at the sculptures and mosaic-decorated walls. And at the quietness with which trains glided through a labyrinth of cool tunnels, like phantoms moving in an underworld trance.

The trance continued as he boarded the trans-Siberian, in the pre-dawn hours. The train journeyed over flatlands of snow, and through the Urals, blanketed in snow. The whole of Russia was under snow. Yet for the passengers it did not seem real. They travelled in comfort. The train was heated. Conductors served hot tea. Those with extra money could purchase vodka as they dined.

Zalman was lulled into a reverie, broken occasionally by a glimpse of stations flitting by. He glanced at the sides of railway tracks along which prisoners trudged under armed guard, their heads bent, their shoulders drawn, their eyes fixed in a helpless gaze. It was a fleeting vision of hell; a brief encounter with the other side, followed by darkness, the pulse of the train, the curving of rails in a rhythmic refrain.

The passengers alighted for an hour in Novosibirsk, deep in central Siberia. The platform seemed deserted. Zalman walked towards the waiting rooms. Without warning he was among crowds of people. They milled about like robots. They moved slowly, as if lost.

Whenever they glanced at Zalman, envy flickered in their eyes. He was well dressed, while they were in rags. He walked with a sense of purpose, while they shuffled aside to let him pass. Others remained squatting on the platform, hunched over their luggage, as if guarding their meagre possessions with their lives. In their eyes, Zalman was from another world. He sensed it, and wanted to reach out and touch them. But instead he recoiled in fear and hurried away.

Day became night became day, and on the following night they moved beyond Irkutsk, along the cusp of Lake Baikal. The lake was covered in ice that glowed under a full moon. The ice shone with blue-white light. There was enough light to read by. Zalman would never forget the details of this night, its stillness, its clarity, the full moon rising above an inland sea.

He stood alone. His fellow passengers were asleep. There was a keenness in the air. In that moment he felt a surge of joy, a subdued excitement. He was on the way to the unknown, yet, as the train drifted by Lake Baikal, he did not care. He did not wish to be elsewhere. He wanted this moment never to end, this moment of journeying in solitude, through calmness, past an unknown sea illumined with lunar light.

At the end of the line loomed Vladivostok, a port city squatting on the eastern rim of the empire. The passengers arrived towards evening and were ordered to remain in their seats. They felt uneasy. Troops patrolled the platform. There were rumours that their visas were invalid, talk of last-minute cancellations. 'We will never leave Russia,' whispered some. 'We are trapped,' murmured others. 'How could we have believed we would be able to escape?'

It was still dark when Zalman and his fellow passengers disembarked. They were ferried in buses to the wharves. The city remained a shadowy presence on the periphery of their vision. Here and there they registered the twinkle of lights and street lamps. Before them stretched the black waters of the bay.

The passengers were hurried towards the wharves. They cast their eyes down so as not to meet the customs police's gaze; and they kept quiet. It was the silence of those who have lost the power to determine their fate.

As a grey dawn broke out over the harbour the passengers boarded a Japanese freighter, manned by a Japanese crew. A Russian officer stood by the boarding plank. Zalman presented his documents. The officer tore off the Russian transit visa, and in that instant, Zalman felt it with a startling certainty: this was the moment of no return. He had been severed from the past, from friends, family, and all he had known. He was adrift. He was a refugee. He would always be a refugee.

His only security was his fellow passengers, the three hundred or so he had travelled with from Vilna. They were the last constant. They were exhausted and disoriented. They hovered on the brink of the unknown. But they were together, a herd of kinsfolk, assembled by chance. And in this they found comfort.

Zalman seems like a man permanently perplexed. He sits in Scheherazade on a week-day afternoon. Again he sips his coffee slowly, savouring the taste, savouring his thoughts, devouring the sun that pours through the window. In the years of his retirement, this is what he loves most: to savour, to take his time.

'Our centre of gravity had shifted,' he tells me. 'This is what I sensed as I stood aboard the boat on the day of our departure. The sailors loaded it with freight. Their cargo included a herd of horses. They were led aboard just as we had been, hours earlier. You could see their confusion and fear. We were no different. We were merely animals being shunted about. And our centre of gravity had shifted: away from Poland, Russia, Europe, away from our childhood homes.

'To this day, I no longer have a centre of gravity. I feel rootless. I will always feel rootless. I had been stripped of everything. Of the scent of my youth, my known way of life. And there is a certain advantage in this, a certain freedom. Even today, though I have lived in Melbourne for over fifty years, I have no sense of belonging. I am acutely aware that everything is temporary in life, a mere bridge. One does not build a house on a bridge. Instead I find my true home inside. I escape inside and I can go wherever my fancy takes me.

'You have a taste for champagne, but a pocket only for beer. So the saying goes. But I have enough imagination to make beer taste like champagne. This is the great gift I received. Through losing everything, I became free.

'I no longer care for anthems, and I no longer care even for nations. They too are transient. The truth of who we are lies elsewhere, in the way we order our inner lives as we drift over unknown seas.

'In losing everything, I have come to value everything: to savour this cup of coffee, its warmth, its aroma, to savour my walks by the sea, and this moment with a friend, at a table in Scheherazade. What more is there? Can you tell me?'

The Japanese freighter weighed anchor towards evening. Fragments of debris floated by. Ice breakers swept the bay. The lights of Vladivostok blinked as the vessel moved away. Zalman was afraid he would be sick. But the sea was smooth. The gentle rocking of the boat soothed him.

As they headed out into the darkness Zalman descended into the hold. It was divided by aisles that threaded between rows of straw mats. Passengers lay on the mats. Some were lost in sleep. Others stared at the ceiling. In a dark corner a bearded man, in a black caftan, rocked back and forth in prayer.

Zalman lay down on a mat and fell asleep. He slept deeply. He awoke feeling sick. It was still night. His head ached. His whole body ached. He staggered out onto the deck and vomited. He crawled back onto the straw mat, fell asleep and awoke again, hours later, to a cool sensation on his lips. A fellow passenger was feeding him a slice of apple. He smiled. Zalman has never forgotten that smile or that act of kindness from an older man. A wiser man. Zalman ate the apple and fell back into the darkness.

He awoke again at dawn, and climbed the stairs to the deck. The sea was as smooth as a table. On the horizon he could make out the coastline of Japan. Pine trees rose above distant dunes. The boat floated on a sedate sea. He stood there for hours; he did not know for how long. He had to tear himself away to descend for breakfast.

Zalman returned to the front deck in the late morning. The sun was high. The coast was approaching. He could see forests, fields, wooded hills, a port, and the entrance to a bay. And he thought, 'I am entering the land of Madame Butterfly.'

The Tsuruga wharf drifted towards him in a tranquil dream. Zalman saw the town, its streets lined with wooden houses the colour of teak. He focused on one house. He saw a door. It slid open and he saw a woman in a kimono. She flitted by on wooden clogs. Then she was gone. But in his imagination she remained a luminous presence, a glimpse of the unknown, a Madame Butterfly.

Zalman yearns for peace of mind, but unresolved questions remain, the feeling that he is still on a journey over which he has long lost control. He returns again and again to the moment when he farewelled his loved ones in Warsaw and fled towards the east.

Somehow it was too hasty. There was not time to stop, to register the last image of his mother, the last words of his father, the final sight of familiar streets. How was he to know that it would be forever? This is what has nagged at him for over fifty years. His life has been one long journey away from certainty.

And there is something else. Call it a sense of guilt, perhaps. Call it paradox, an uneasy admission; but there were moments of unexpected elation as he journeyed away from Vilna, moments when he felt an intoxicating surge of freedom. Never was this feeling stronger than on the day he first glimpsed the land of Madame Butterfly.

On the following morning, at dawn, he was escorted from the freighter onto the wharf and through the deserted streets of Tsuruga. They walked, a party of three hundred or more, through the sleeping town. They walked along narrow streets lined with rows of wooden houses. Miniature bridges looped over cement ditches to the entrance of each dwelling. A lone woman swept the street in front of a store. Two fishermen trudged to the beach front, their nets draped over their backs. Behind the town loomed hills over which the sun had yet to rise.

Their lives were in the hands of customs officers and railway-men, of Japanese authorities and Jewish relief workers who directed them through the gates of the station. They marched to the end of a platform and, exactly on time, to the very minute, the train arrived.

The doors opened. The refugees filed in and sat down, each one on a seat of their own. This is what struck Zalman, the effi-ciency, the precision, the politeness; and cleanliness. More than ever he felt as though he was moving in a dream.

The train crawled over mountain passes. Zalman caught glimpses of cascading waterfalls and gorges. He saw pines bent back by centuries of wind. He saw fields criss-crossed with flooded paddies. Peasants stood in the fields, dressed in high boots, colourful blouses and pyjama-style pants. He saw women with white headscarves and sashes tied around their waists. He glimpsed clusters of cottages, their tiled roofs cast in mauve and turquoise tints. He saw the ruins of a castle, the lush gardens of a villa. He caught sight of wooden temples, and pilgrims gathered about a shrine.

The train approached industrial complexes smudged with smoke. Open fields gave way to city thoroughfares and milling crowds. The train slowed to a halt, the doors parted. The refugees filed out. They were met on the platform by relief workers who escorted them out of the station and through the streets of Kobe.

They walked under a winter sun, stateless men and women in transit. They walked exposed to its glare, unaccustomed to the light, their eyes blinking. They walked in their crumpled clothes, the shabby suits they had worn since they left Vilna.

Among them walked yeshiva boys in black pants, white shirts and narrow-brimmed hats, clutching prayer books wrapped in embroidered bags. Beside them walked rabbis clad in black satin coats, and a scattering of children, the girls in head kerchiefs and frayed dresses, the boys in knickerbockers and worn jackets. The children moved hand-in-hand with self-appointed guardians, or with their mothers and fathers, those numbered few with families intact.

Mostly they were single men who, like Zalman, could not erase the faces of dear ones. These were the images that plagued their minds as they ascended a steep incline. Below them, coming into view, was yet another harbour. The vista expanded as they climbed. The harbour was crowded with gunboats and freighters.

The bay glowed under a sheen of silver. The strip of fore-shore extended inland, several hundred metres flat, before ascending into the hills up which they trudged. They moved past houses flying the flags of France and Britain, of Switzerland, Denmark and Norway. They were in the international quarters, among the homes of merchants and diplomats, wealthy traders and shipping agents.

As they climbed, Zalman was overwhelmed by a sense of wonder. The entire day had been a reverie. He had been entranced by the beauty about him, the symmetry. He had been seduced into a sense of security, of being in capable hands. He had journeyed through a land of strange gods and fast-flowing streams. Yet, like so many of the men about him, he could not forsake the thought of those they had left behind with the promise of better days.

They still clung to that hope. They talked politics incessantly. They clutched at every possibility. They fantasised about moving to America, Australia, Canada or Palestine. At night they lay on tatami mats and conjured impossible futures; and they arose each morning from the homes the Jews of Kobe had rented for them, within the European settlement, and descended to the community centre.

It stood at the foot of the hills, a cluster of rooms in a narrow lane. They would come to know it well, the several thousand refugees who were to pass through Kobe in the spring and summer of 1941. They spent many hours in these rooms where they filled in forms, read papers and listened intently to communal radios, to each shred of news.

Zalman can still see the cramped offices, the metal filing cabinets, the battered wooden desks. He can smell the kerosene heaters and feel the morning sun through the windows, relieving the gloom. And to this day he can recall the pounding of his heart, as he stood, each morning afresh, at the communal bulletin board, in the hope of a message from 'home', thousands of kilometres to the west.

Zalman would scan the board, shrug his shoulders, and move out into the streets. The news was rarely good. The armies of the Third Reich continued their murderous drive. Visa applications were being rejected, doors were being sealed. What else was there to do but walk?

He walked past stalls laden with bananas and tangerines. He stopped at shops selling herbs and spices he had never smelt before. He inhaled the aroma of fried foods sold by market vendors who lined the way. He wandered lanes teeming with women in grey kimonos, ferrying babies upon their backs. He saw passers-by dressed in army jackets and khaki pants. Radios blared martial music. Makeshift cooking stoves lined the sidewalks. The scent of frying fish curdled the air. Bicycles and rickshaws thronged the streets. A military motorcade glided by.

He descended to the flatlands and walked towards docks lined with military hardware. Tanks and artillery sweated under tarpaulins. Warehouses sprawled beside the wharves. Officers strutted the foreshore.

Zalman returned to the heights. He traced a well-worn path to a neighbourhood park. He sat on a bench overlooking the harbour. He gazed at hillside cottages tiled in crimson and blue. He noted the strands of bamboo, the beds of camellias in full bloom. He observed the first buds of plum blossoms. His treks would always end here, by the park bench, overlooking the city.

At nightfall Zalman would return to the two-storey brick house he shared with a group of single men and two families. Directly opposite stood a house occupied by Germans. On a white pole, above the roof, fluttered the Nazi flag. They would pass each other occasionally, German merchants and stateless Jews, without uttering a word; and more than ever, Zalman felt that he was living in an illusion, within a remote kingdom into which he had blundered by pure chance. There was nothing he could do but bide his time. Walk. Embark on excursions to the hinterland.

He joined a group of friends on an outing to the resort town of Takarasuka, renowned for its women's theatre. The town was ablaze with spring blossoms. Zalman sat with his group of companions in the Takarasuka Grand Theatre and gazed at a revolving stage on which they saw epic battles between Samurai warriors, Moulin Rouge-style can-can chorus lines, gladiatorial contests set in ancient Rome, and Broadway-inspired song-and-dance routines, performed in an eccentric theatrical amalgam of west and east. The boundaries of the world seemed to be dissolving. The foundations were melting beneath his feet.

On one of his walks Zalman came across a small cafe, a cluster of seats in a dimly lit room. He was drawn inside by the sounds of a Schubert sonata. A Japanese woman dressed in a kimono served ice-cream sodas and ersatz coffee. When the music ceased she returned to the record player and replaced the sonata with a Chopin polonaise.

There were six clients before him, awaiting their turn. When their request had been played, they moved on to make way for new customers. The waitress approached Zalman and handed him a booklet filled with a list of titles. He chose the final movement of a Tchaikovsky concerto.

The cafe was the brainchild of a Japanese with a passion for classical music. Signs on the wall indicated it was forbidden to talk. If a customer disobeyed, the owner would stop the music and frown. The cafe was for music lovers only.

Zalman became more attuned to the nuances of the senses. He began to discover, on his daily walks, crevices of peace: the tinkling of a wind chime, the sight of Shinto priests hurrying by, otherworldly in their white gowns and black hats; a glimpse of an old man in a secluded garden; the chant of a Buddhist monk echoing from a neighbourhood temple; the sing-song prayers of rabbinical scholars from Poland, flowing from their temporary house of worship.

Zalman had been raised in a family of free thinkers, of socialists and secular Jews. Yet he could recognise in both the Buddhist chants and the Hebrew prayers the same yearning for harmony in a world gone mad. He heard it also in the music cafe, during his frequent visits: that particular moment within the trembling echo of a single note; a moment of sudden clarity and pure tone.

It was in the cafe, between recordings, that he was told by a fellow patron that a Japanese opera company in Osaka, a city thirty kilometres from Kobe, was to perform Giuseppe Verdi's *La Traviata*. Zalman would never forget the details of the following day. In the morning he collected money from fellow opera lovers among the refugees and travelled to Osaka to purchase the tickets.

When he arrived at the Osaka station, Zalman approached a policeman directing traffic in the middle of a busy intersection, and asked him the way to the Kabuki-za theatre. The policeman halted the traffic and guided him to a tram stop. He remained with Zalman until he found someone who could direct him further.

A bystander escorted him onto a tram. Fifteen minutes later they arrived at the theatre. Zalman purchased the tickets and that evening he returned from Kobe, with his party of friends, to attend the opera.

The Japanese performers looked somewhat stiff and uncomfortable in their rendition of Italian arias. Yet there was an addictive charm about their attempts to emulate a culture far removed from their own. The performance worked its own magic. Arias came to resemble hypnotic chants. The fluid movements of the west slid into the stylised stage movements of the east. The conventions of European opera merged with the rituals of a Kabuki play. Zalman was entranced.

After the performance he wandered the streets of Osaka with his companions. They savoured the summer air. 'A year ago who would have thought it possible,' they mused, 'that we would be watching *La Traviata* in Japan?' They returned to Kobe in high spirits, and the following evening they learnt that the armies of the Third Reich had invaded Russia.

As they began to absorb the news on that June night, in the Japanese summer of 1941, they knew their world could no longer be the same. Within days they heard that sections of Vilna were in flames. More than ever they were isolated from the loved ones they had left behind. More than ever they were plagued by a sense of guilt and unbearable longing.

The route back to the old world was cut off. Ships could no longer make the journey from Vladivostok to Tsuruga. The American option had dried up as relations with Japan soured. Curaçao was beyond reach. The Japanese were being pressured by their German allies to deal more harshly with refugees. In frantic negotiations behind the scenes, between Jewish community leaders and Japanese authorities, one last option was agreed upon.

On 17 September 1941, after an interlude of seven months, Zalman and his companions descended from their hillside homes to the harbour, suitcases clutched in their hands. It was an autumn day. Kobe glistened in auburns and golds. The city seemed distant and calm. Again they were strangers, detached from the mainstream, captive to a journey beyond their control.

The refugees boarded the passenger ship, the *Taiyo Maru*. Towards evening they stood on the decks gazing at their former haven on the heights. They watched until the widening gap extinguished the last receding lights; and as he recalls that moment, Zalman pauses, and lapses into stillness, as if reliving his sense of resignation, and the helplessness he had felt as the *Taiyo Maru* made its way into the darkness towards the South China Sea.

Even as we sit and drink and argue and talk at the tables of Scheherazade, even as I continue to listen to their tales, they are moving on, the old men. One by one they are going. Every few weeks I hear of another death. I have been drawn into their collective fate. I follow them to the cemetery that sprawls at the southern fringe of the city, an hour's drive from the cafe.

I have farewelled them in all seasons now: on spring days, following the funeral bier along paths sprouting weeds and errant flowers. On days of summer heat, over paths hardened and parched. On winter mornings under skies sagging with clouds, the mud sucking at the shoes, the gravesides sodden with clay. And on autumn afternoons, the sun low on the northern horizon, the paths gilded with plant decay.

The cemetery stands on a flat plain. To the north rise the hills of the Dandenong Ranges. On clear days they appear like cardboard cut-outs, lit up in startling focus against expansive skies. On such days I glimpse the final irony in the old men's journeys, the final twist in the tale.

They had come from the old world to the new to remake their shattered lives. Yet it can be sensed, by their gravesides, that this too is an ageing land; worn low by geological time into wooded hills and basalt plains, its features suffused with its own peculiar light which illumines the rabbi intoning the funeral rites.

His voice dissipates in the wind. Eulogies evaporate mid-air. One by one old friends step up to shovel the freshly dug earth over the pine casket. Those that step back converse quietly in this moment of suspended time.

As the mourners depart, two attendants complete the task of covering the grave. Within minutes all that remains is a mound of earth topped by a wooden stave. The crowd has dispersed. A generation is moving on. And with each passing life I feel it more keenly: there are tales aching to be told, craving to be heard, before they too disappear into the grave.

So I return to the cafe, to the remaining storytellers, to listen and record. To inscribe and pass on. And, in so doing, to add to the mythology of an ancient land.

When I ask him to recall the years he spent in Shanghai, Zalman is somewhat vague. 'Shanghai? What stands out? What impressions come to mind? The confusion. Where Kobe was symmetry, Shanghai was chaos. Where Kobe was an idyllic interlude, Shanghai was a rat's maze, a dead-end.

'Martin, if I were a painter trying to depict Shanghai in the war years, I would plunge my brush into all the colours of the palette and splash them on thick, at random. Or if I were a musician I would take all the instruments from all over the world, put them together, and say, "Hey! Blow! Scream! Bang! Play as loud as you can! All of you!"

'What more can I say? In Shanghai I had a persistent feeling of wanting to run away. I felt as if I was stuck in a swamp. Shanghai was the lowest ebb, and within its chaos I had to surrender, to let go of all hope. Yet, in Shanghai, strangely enough, I rediscovered the moments of solitude I had learnt to recognise on my daily walks through the streets of Kobe.'

Again the wrinkling brow as Zalman speaks; again that look of awe tinged with irony as he contemplates a journey which continues to flow through him, and still surprises him with its capacity to flood his mind.

After a journey of thirty-six hours the *Taiyo Maru* entered the mouth of the Whangpoo River. Zalman noted the stillness of the water, its coffee-like texture, the bat-winged sailing junks littering the port. He saw families crowded upon the junks, their drying clothes hanging from makeshift lines. He saw barges bulging with coal, piloted by river-men whose faces were black with dust and sun-beaten toil. Freighters and liners edged to and from a drift of warehouses and docks. Single-oared sampans darted in and out like audacious dwarfs.

In the foreground he could hear the lapping of the water, a sound which seemed all the more alluring in the midst of so much noise. And there was the heat. He had never experienced anything like it before, a damp heat that dripped with fatigue and blunted the senses.

The *Taiyo Maru* rounded a sharp bend and came upon a riverside boulevard alight with trolley cars and rickshaws hauled by Chinese labourers on the trot. Coolies ran with loads bouncing from shoulder poles. The sun bounced off their lithe bodies, which were saturated in sweat. British and French overlords walked by, perspiring in formal attire. European-style buildings, opulent banks and houses of trade, adorned with domes and cupolas, arched windows and bas-relief pillars, towered over the thoroughfare.

As Zalman gazed upon this inferno of commerce, the *Taiyo Maru* anchored offshore. The Kobe refugees descended into motor launches and were transferred to the waterfront. It was the same at every border, that feeling of insignificance, of being at the mercy of uniformed officers bloated by their status and the power they wielded.

Even members of the Jewish refugee relief committees, on hand to greet them, seemed irritable. They directed the newcomers into open-sided trucks that lurched into the traffic of Shanghai. The convoy carried them past a sweep of consulates, onto the Garden Bridge over Suzhou Creek. A fleet of junks moved by, laden with timber and coal. Beyond the polluted waters they glimpsed the alleys that were to become so familiar in the ensuing four years.

The trucks slowed to a halt in the district of Hongkew. Just four years earlier, it had been the site of bloody battles fought between Japanese armies and the defending Chinese. The invaders rampaged through Hongkew in a fury. Up to a quarter of a million Chinese fell in the assault. As they retreated, they torched buildings that were about to fall into enemy hands.

The new Hongkew rose from the ruins, an insanity of makeshift houses interspersed with vacant lots covered in charred ruins and rubbish dumps. There were dwellings that seemed to remain frozen in a bloodstained past; doors hung from their hinges; breezes whistled through gaping holes. In the typhoon season, mud and water gutted the streets. In the summer months, the smell of food and refuse rose like poisonous vapour from the hardened earth.

Perhaps one hundred thousand Chinese lived in this dilapidated area, alongside an escalating population of refugees. In the late 1930s seventeen thousand Jews, denied entry to the rest of the world, had streamed into Shanghai. They had fled from Germany, Austria, Czechoslovakia, from Vienna, Prague and Berlin, from towns and cities scattered throughout Nazi-occupied Europe.

They had journeyed by foot, on rail, by riverboat or automobile. They had dodged authorities, bribed officials, paid exit taxes, obtained visas by means fair or foul. They had crossed mountains, stumbled upon detours, rescued themselves from cul-de-sacs. They had grasped every slim chance to move closer to the one destination on earth where entrance papers were still not required. Until, at long last, they awoke to find themselves drifting along the Whangpoo towards the Shanghai river-port.

Like Zalman, many of them had been greeted by relief workers who sent them on their way across Garden Bridge, to their assigned places within an array of converted warehouses, factories, boarding houses and terraced cottages clinging to shabby lanes. They spent their first months in partitioned rooms crowded with double bunks, inhaling the damp night air or huddling under blankets to ward off the unexpected winter cold. Theirs was a fragile haven, built upon charity and foundations of blood; but it was a haven, nevertheless.

Yet, for Zalman, Shanghai remained a place of despair. This was the feeling that took hold of him as soon as he entered Hongkew. It was a thought that was to become an obsession during his four-year stay. More than half a century later all that remains are a string of images, random almost, punctuated by a number of crucial dates that marked the gradual erosion of whatever optimism Zalman still possessed.

At first he lived in a warehouse reserved for single men. Later he moved in with a family of three, from Warsaw—Hadassah, Yasha and their only son, twelve-year-old Chaim—who had managed to stay together on the entire journey from Vilna to Shanghai.

They lived in a windowless room in Hongkew, separated from adjoining cubicles by plywood partitions and curtains suspended from bamboo poles. Through the slim partitions could be heard the clatter of dishes, the shrill voices of couples arguing, the sounds of love-making, the echo of footsteps on the rickety wooden stairs. Seeping through the crevices came the smell of coal dust, of cinders and burnt straw, of fried foods and rancid oil, billowing from primitive stoves which provided just enough sustenance for the slum-dwellers to survive.

And, for a while, some of them thrived. The refugees moved freely in and out of the international and French concessions which still remained in European hands. Zalman found work in the offices of a Russian firm trading in furs. Chinese labourers, the universal underclass, salted weasel skins and mink. The treated furs were stored in warehouses for future export. Zalman co-ordinated the shipments, kept accounts and, when there was nothing to do, which was often enough, he would rest his feet on the desk, light a cigarette and lean back in his chair. Or he would lock the door behind him and stroll out onto the streets.

War-time Shanghai was a city sustained by speculation and wheeler-dealing, gambling and black marketeering. Shanghai was living on borrowed time.

'You could feel it,' says Zalman. 'The city was unhinged. There were even buildings rising from concrete rafts which, in turn, floated on mud flats. In the side streets, abandoned children covered in sores ran in packs. Beggars tugged at your sleeves. I saw the desperation in their eyes. Those who were making a living hurried by. They did not look. They did not wish to see. Those well-off snuggled back in their cars on their way to the cabarets and private clubs.

'But for some reason it has been my fate to detect the destitution beneath the gaiety; to be drawn towards it, to walk through it; to turn into Blood Alley, in the French concession, where drunken sailors staggered after streetwalkers. The sailors roamed the city in gangs. They crowded into dance halls in pursuit of "sing-song girls". They drank and made merry, and lived each day as if it was their last. Yet to me they seemed like *dybbuks*, lost spirits in search of a warm body to possess so far from home.

'As for Hongkew, it was a carnival of *dybbuks*. I wandered its streets, to and from my place of work. We were a kingdom of dung beetles, scurrying about, doing what we could to survive; and Hongkew was our dung heap. I would walk past Chinese families who slept in vacant lots. I stepped over dead babies wrapped in newspapers or bamboo mats. The morning air was permeated with the smell of our night shit dripping from sewerage tanks. Porters groaned as they hauled their carts. Women hurried to work with babies tied to their backs.

'All the while, we continued to dream the dream of the displaced. A dream which stole through the narrow alleys of Hongkew in the early hours, when the noise subsided, and a shallow sleep overtook us: a dream of horizons and ports, of ample decks fanned by sea breezes.

'The dreamers leaned against the rails. In their hands glittered the longed-for treasure, a visa to new worlds. They were sailing towards sanctuaries where the streets flowed with freedom. And they awoke to their dank cubicles, their crowded dormitories, and the rising cacophony of another futureless day.'

The cold rains descended, the north winds took hold and, in the early hours of 8 December 1941, Japanese planes attacked Pearl Harbor. In the pre-dawn darkness Japanese troops lined Shanghai's riverside boulevard and launched an assault upon the sole US naval vessel, moored mid-river. They opened fire on the Royal Navy gunboat, the HMS *Peterel*, anchored further upstream. Outnumbered on all sides, the boat sank in flames. The river glowed in its after-light. Some of the crew were swept downstream as they swam for the shore, where they were captured, and ferried to the infamous Ward Road jail.

At dawn a squadron of planes released leaflets with the news that 'an unfortunate state of war has come about between Japan and the Allies. Do not panic.'

As the Year of the Serpent drew to an end the refugees of Shanghai were too weary to panic. There was no longer any place upon earth to which they could run. The international concessions had fallen into Japanese hands. The prized city was firmly under their command.

During 1942 the refugees of Shanghai lived in limbo. Their fates were determined according to rapidly shifting definitions of nationality. Those with British, American or French passports were driven out of the city into internment camps. Russian emigres remained in the former concessions, free to work in businesses now transferred into Japanese control. And those who had, at first, escaped definition, those categorised as stateless, awoke on 18 February 1943 to radio bulletins proclaiming the establishment of a ghetto, in a 'Designated District' within Hongkew.

Wall posters echoed the news. All Polish, Austrian, Czech and German Jews who had arrived in Shanghai since 1937 had until 18 May to move into a forty-block area. Their movements were now monitored by Japanese troops, Sikh police, and a patrol of sentries drafted from the ghetto inmates.

Zalman spent his nights with Hadassah, Yasha and Chaim. They played chess and draughts, reminisced about Warsaw, shared their meagre rations of food. In the mornings, Zalman would leave his cramped quarters, descend the stairs, and move out into the streets of Hongkew. He returned to his incessant walking; and he knew what he was looking for: those crevices of solitude he had discovered during his walks in Kobe.

In the Shanghai of 1943 such moments were all but impossible to find. Japanese officers strutted about with the arrogant air that characterises occupying forces. The order which had impressed Zalman in Kobe gave way to random checks and indiscriminate beatings. A system of passes restricted movement to and from the ghetto gates. The streets of Hongkew teemed with children fossicking through rubble. Typhus and cholera, beriberi and dysentery claimed many lives. Others died of hunger, heat exhaustion and despair, while those without work sat day after day in ghetto coffee shops and played cards.

And through it all Zalman walked. He walked beside barbed-wire fences and past soldiers clutching bayonets. He walked the lanes of Hongkew, and beyond, into the city at large, whenever he was able to wrangle a pass from the Japanese police. He walked from dawn to dusk, day after week after month, and he returned each night to the windowless room that was his home. This was his one constant, a family, three people to whom he had grown close. But the room was oppressive. Zalman could not wait for the night curfew to end; he would often leave before first light.

It was at dawn that he came upon the image he was looking for. It emerged from a damp fog that lingered over Suzhou Creek. Boats hovered in the mist. A solitary junk moved by, weighed down beneath a mountainous cargo of hay.

On the banks of the creek, Zalman saw a figure trudging over a desolate stretch of earth. In his right hand he carried a birdcage. The old man came to a halt by a tree. He took off his jacket and hung it on the lower branches beside the cage. The trill of a songbird flowed through the bars.

The old man lifted his arms, lowered his upper body and bent his knees. His back remained upright as he glided from form to form, in a slow-motion dance that seemed to defy the routine laws of movement. His legs remained bent at the knee, so that his lower body seemed anchored to the earth, while his upper body floated free, like a bird in flight.

Zalman followed each movement intently. For a moment Shanghai stood still; and Zalman rediscovered his poise. It was a mere fifteen minutes before the Chinaman ceased his movements. Unhurried, he put on his jacket, retrieved the birdcage, and trudged back through the rising mist.

Then he was gone; and although Zalman returned, day after day, at the same time, to the same strip of waterfront beside the creek, he never saw the old man again. He had to content himself with the image. He could conjure it at any time; and with it came the comfort of knowing that such moments could still exist.

In June 1944, the first Allied air raids hit Shanghai. American bombers targeted warehouses, factories and munitions dumps with remarkable precision. By early 1945 the allied armies were well on the advance. Manila fell in February. Iwo Jima in March. By April, Chinese armies were turning their sights back towards Shanghai.

On a searingly hot July day in 1945, pedestrians on the streets of Hongkew would have glimpsed above them shafts of sunlight reflecting silver from the wings of American planes. A diamond formation of bombers broke away and veered towards the shore. Sirens signalled the alert. The planes streaked over Hongkew and tilted towards the intersection of Tongshan and Kung Ping roads.

Below them, Zalman and his adopted family joined a frantic rush of refugees into the corridors of a community centre. They had just finished lunch. They huddled in the corridors.

Hadassah stayed behind in the kitchen. She remained wedded to her chores. Perhaps this is what saved her.

Zalman retains a clear picture of what ensued. He recalls conversations, word for word. He hears the muffled explosions. He sees the corridor, in detail, as it is thrust into darkness. He remembers the uneasy calm, riddled with dust. Zalman clutched at the man standing next to him.

'Let go of me,' said the man.

'We are all covered in dust,' said Zalman. 'Look. Over there. There's a light.'

'I am wounded,' replied the man. And he turned, and ran.

Zalman saw two figures lying nearby. One was Yasha, his surrogate father. He lay motionless. The other, fifteen-year-old Chaim, was covered in blood.

'I can't feel my leg,' said Chaim. 'Go and see how mother is doing,' he added. 'Tell her father is dead. Tell her I am wounded. Don't let her see me.'

Zalman rushed to the kitchen. 'Yasha is dead. Chaim is wounded. I will take care of him. Just stay where you are.'

'I will do as you say,' Hadassah replied. Her voice seemed distant. She filled a bucket with water, seized a brush, sank to her knees, and began to scrub the floor. She scrubbed as if possessed. Zalman was struck by her calmness. She continued to work. She was bent over like a rabbi, lost in prayer, but when she briefly lifted her head, he glimpsed the horror in her eyes.

Zalman returned to the corridor. He lifted Chaim onto a door that had been blown off its hinges. A friend helped him carry the boy out to the streets. They barely registered the panic and the noise. They barely noticed the buildings in flames, the casualties laid out on blankets, the bodies scattered over the centre's vegetable garden.

Rickshaw drivers cleared a passage. At the periphery of his vision Zalman saw corpses strewn over the streets. He glimpsed his Chinese neighbours, as if from afar. They were running with sheets and shirts, towels and skirts, which they tore into bandages as they headed for the wounded.

The two men carrying Chaim were directed to a makeshift aid centre, hastily set up in the grounds of the Ward Road jail. Charred bodies lay beside the injured: men, women and children huddled together in the prison yard. Above them loomed watchtowers, barred windows and grey walls. Refugee doctors and nurses tended the victims.

Chaim was lifted off the stretcher. Zalman noted the massive wound in the abdomen. He saw the liver, exposed. A young woman, a doctor, knelt down by Chaim's side.

'I will live,' murmured the boy.

'Leave him with me,' said the doctor. 'I will take care of him. And you?'

'There is nothing wrong with me,' replied Zalman.

'You are bleeding all over.'

For the first time Zalman felt the pain, the numbness in his face. For the first time he observed his own wounds, the shrapnel, the patches of blood.

The doctor injected Zalman with anti-tetanus serum. 'I will

operate on the boy. Come back in an hour.'

'I will live,' murmured Chaim.

Zalman returned an hour later to learn that Chaim had briefly regained consciousness; he had died just minutes earlier.

A blazing July day in 1945. The war was all but over. Zalman had lost his second family. There was nowhere to go. There was nothing to hope for. There was no need to hurry. There was nothing to do but walk.

VI

Scheherazade is a Babel of languages. Each one has its peculiar melody, its distinct tone. Polish and Russian are cool languages. They flow like the Dnieper, the Volga, the Vistula, and the River Bug. German, with its polysyllables, seems to be forever grasping at grandiose abstractions. I hear smatterings of Hungarian and Romanian, and tongues entirely foreign to my ears. And I register countless varieties of English, seasoned by many accents and tongues.

As for Yiddish, it is the main course. A frantic language, propelled by manic winds and enforced flight, a hybrid, concocted on the run. With bits of this, pieces of that: Slavic, a large dose of Germanic, a hint of the Ukraine, and an echo of the Asiatic steppes. With residues of biblical Hebrew, and other ancient tongues. It is a language of wanderers, of Gypsies, *tsigeiner.*

'I am a *tsigeiner,*' says Yossel Bartnowski. 'I love to be on the move, always in search of greener fields.'

And he sings:

'Carefree is the *tsigeiner's* life.
Farria!
We do not have the Kaiser, taxes to pay.

Farria!
Carefree it is in the forests, green
Where *tsigeiners* will be dancing soon.
Farria. Farria. Farria. Farria.
Far-ri-ya-ha-ha-ha-ha-ha.'

Today Yossel is clothed in varying tones of white. He wears a white shirt and cream slacks, an off-white tie and white shoes. He places his white-brimmed hat on the table. His blue eyes are darting about, following the ladies moving past on the street. He glances at the patrons entering the cafe, and surveys the chicken schnitzel that the mini-skirted waitress places by his side. 'Thank you, my beautiful girl,' he says, with a wink. 'Isn't she a *krasavetze,* a true beauty?'

He unfolds a serviette, and sings:

'Farria. Farria. Farria. Farria.
Far-ri-ya-ha-ha-ha-ha-ha.'

We sit in Scheherazade's alcove, at the window table, mid-afternoon on a hot autumn day. Its light penetrates the back room where Masha and Avram are entertaining friends. It seeps into the kitchen where the yeast hardens in electric ovens and pans sizzle on leaping flames; it creeps into the back lane where last night's leftovers lie fermenting in rubbish bins. It is a naked light, hard and hot. But here, in the alcove, it is airconditioned, cool.

We sit at a round table, a perfect fit, with ample room. We can stretch and yawn and swivel about. It is an ideal viewing place, surrounded by plate-glass frontage and glass doors enclosed in wooden frames. Window reflections obscure us from the view of those who pass by on the pavement outside.

'Ah, what a wonderful *meshugas*,' says Yossel. 'What a *mekhaiye* it is to sit and watch. What a pure delight. This is why I have always loved cafes on busy streets.'

A man hurries past, holding his spectacles in one hand, a briefcase in the other, in a permanent state of readiness. A teenage couple, in school uniform, stroll by hand-in-hand. A woman in a black suit, white ribbon in her hair, clatters past on white high heels, with a white poodle in tow. The poodle's head sprouts a black bow.

'Now that, my dear Martin, is the way to dress,' says Yossel. He swivels his head from side to side. 'Ah, what an exquisite girl, the one in the low-cut red blouse. What a *krasavetze*. Look at the way she glides by. What a *mekhaiye*. Red is the best colour for such an aristocrat.

'I do not like being alone,' he adds a moment later, 'to sit at home in my apartment. I was born surrounded by people. I have always delighted in crowds. My foolish child, I am a Krochmalna boy. I love life. I want to enjoy myself, to use my allotted time.

'And I love people. Especially girls. Look at the princess in the leather shorts. Ah, such rounded hips; such *sheine fisslakh*, such beautiful legs.'

Yossel sinks his teeth into the schnitzel. 'Scheherazade is a schnitzel *gan eiden*,' he says, 'a schnitzel paradise. It has the best. And every variety. My favourite is the chicken. But, if you wish, you can have veal schnitzel, a Parisian schnitzel, a Wiener schnitzel. Or you can order your own, the way you once had it, over there, homemade, in *der alter velt*.'

He pauses for another ample bite. 'And they are honest schnitzels, saturated with oil, swimming in juice, with big portions, and no skimping. Look how it fills the whole plate; it even sticks out over the side. My dear Martin, one thing I know, when there is food, don't be shy. Who knows if you will ever enjoy another meal. Here, have a bite.'

'I am a vegetarian,' I say.

'You are a fool,' he replies. 'In nature it is eat or be eaten. This is what I learnt on Krochmalna Street. This is what I discovered, all over again, in Vilna and Vladivostok, in Kobe and Shanghai. This is what I have seen in every city I have passed through in this *meshugene velt*. So, don't worry. Have a bite. It won't hurt.'

Yossel too made the journey from Vilna to the east as a Sugihara Jew. But he and Zalman travelled separately. Except for their meetings in Wolfke's they lived very different lives. They had not known each other in Warsaw where they grew up in neighbourhoods far apart. Yossel was schooled in the run-down tenements of pre-war Krochmalna Street, where the dividing line between society and underworld was thin. This is where he first learnt to live by his wits, to sniff the air and know what was what.

Like so many others, Yossel had fled Warsaw in September 1939. Vilna was a place to draw breath, a footstep beyond the newly drawn borders that divided the Nazi-occupied west from the Soviet east.

'My foolish child, Vilna was a poor city. There was not enough fuel to make a fire. We would buy a kettle full of hot water and drop in a sweet as sugar. We slept in houses of prayer, in corridors and foyers. We slept in apartments, ten to a room. I lay down wherever I could and, when I woke up, I went out and sniffed the air. I have always relied on my nose. It has never let me down.

'My nose led me to Wolfke's. Perhaps it was the aroma of food. In Wolfke's you could buy the best cholent in Vilna, a delicious stew of onions, potatoes and beans, barley and beef. And their chopped liver was exquisite! With mashed boiled eggs, as smooth as pate. Such a delicacy. A true delight.

'I knew this could not last long. Soon we were living on crusts of bread. But in Wolfke's I made contacts. I began to deal on the black market. I bought and sold currency, tobacco, anything that came my way. One thing led to another and I found myself in a shop selling nuts and bolts, screws and tacks, nails and knick-knacks.

'I got to know the woman who ran the shop. She was called Dvora, a biblical name. She looked like the women of those times. She was beautiful. I fell in love with her at first sight. I have often fallen in love at first sight. Why waste time? Life is short.

'Dvora had an agent who supplied her with goods, a

Lithuanian. He sold us diamonds at fifty dollars a carat. I smuggled them from Vilna, to the most elegant hotel in Kovno, where a German buyer paid double the price. Dvora became my sweetheart. We made a lot of money.'

Yossel speaks Yiddish in a Warsaw dialect I strain to understand. The elegance of his clothes belies his Krochmalna Street roots. This was the secret to his success, he tells me—to dress elegantly. Good dress came before food.

'People liked me,' he says. 'This was the great thing, to be well dressed and have charm. This is why people trust you, why people buy from you. First you establish a liking for each other, then you do business.'

Yossel is on the cusp of ninety, yet the charm is still evident. It is not a calculated charm, but rather the boyish charm of a gambler.

'I have always taken risks. I was willing to step out into the world. Whenever I saw a window I looked through it. If I saw an open door, I was not shy. Whenever I saw a cafe, I stepped in.

'I wanted to leave Vilna, get out of Europe, sail to the ends of the earth. I could see it was all crumbling. Meanwhile I needed money. With money you can help yourself, and help others. Without money, you are *gornisht*, nothing. This is what I learnt from the boys of Krochmalna. This is what we schemed about in the basement cafe in the Polonia hotel. Do you think we had a choice?

'In Vilna I made money. In Vilna I lost money. I was arrested three times. Three times I managed to wriggle free. Our contacts in the diamond business dried up. The Nazis, may they rot in *gehennim*, were perilously close. I could smell the approaching fear. I sniffed the air and I could sense what was what. It was time to get out.

'We heard that there was a way via the Baltic. A fisherman would smuggle us over to Sweden. Then we heard that Germans and Lithuanians were intercepting those who were trying to escape, and shooting them on the spot. Wherever we turned there was a trap.

'Then in Wolfke's the talk turned to a man called Sugihara. May he sit with full honours by God's right side! May his feet be forever massaged by angels and cherubim. He was a true *tzaddik*. A saint!

'My dear Martin, of course I met him in person. First, I had to obtain a pass to Curaçao, a Dutch colony. I am sure Zalman has told you about this. He knows every little detail. He still reads books about it.

'I took the train from Vilna to Kovno and dashed to the office of the Dutch consul, Mr Zwartendyk. I never forget a name. He was a businessman. He sold radios and lightbulbs but I was in too much of a hurry to talk and do deals. I ran straight to Sugihara's. I joined the many hundreds gathered outside his Kovno home. I hopped about as if standing on pins. I sweated and jostled along with the impatient crowd. And Sugihara welcomed us all. He was a true *tzaddik*! A man of pure gold! He stamped whatever we put under his nose.

'When I left Sugihara's I was dancing in the streets. I was *meshuge* with relief. I kept patting my pocket, to make sure my precious papers were still there. I slept with them under my pillow. I wrapped them in a waterproof bag.

'Every few days I would take them out and kiss them one by one. I kept them with me day and night. I had found a passageway to wonderland. The papers had cost me only the price of a return ticket from Vilna to Kovno, but they were worth far more than gold. It was a *metziah*! The best bargain I have ever struck in my life!

'Months later I went to the Vilna offices of the NKVD. I was terrified. Everyone was afraid of them. But without their approval we could not leave. They worked twenty-four hours a day. They interrogated you in their cold rooms. They glared at you with hard eyes.

'But I had *mazel*. I have always had good luck. The man who interviewed me was a Jewish officer. And I charmed him. I spoke to him in Yiddish, the mother tongue. I made him feel as though I was his long-lost son. My foolish child, I was desperate. And I knew what I had to do! After all, I am a Krochmalna boy.

'A few days later a friend came running to me. He was jumping with joy. "Yossel, we are on the list," he told me. We had found a way out of our black hole. We celebrated by drinking a bottle of vodka. Or was it two? Ah, never before had I so relished its bitter taste. Vodka is a medicine. It can cure colds, relieve boredom, and prepare an old man for the act of love.

'By the time we swallowed the last drop we were flying. We flew to the police station by horse-drawn droshkies. We flew over the snow to the tinkling of bells. We received our exit visas in style. The NKVD officer shook my hand, and wished me a bon voyage and good luck. I have always known how to draw people to me.

'I received the visa on a Wednesday. On the Thursday, I went to my Dvora and bought the remaining diamonds. She did not want to come with me. Vilna was her home. We said our good-byes, and I never saw her again. My dear Martin, this is how it was.

'On Friday I went to a yeshiva boy who made special suit-cases. They contained secret compartments in which I hid diamonds, American dollars and English pounds. I packed in salami, tins of goose fat, bottles of vodka, a flagon of cognac: all the delicacies a traveller requires.

'The next day I took the three suitcases to the train. I had purchased a ticket for a princely sum. I paid over two hundred dollars, American. But it was worth it. I had privileges. I had comfort. I travelled first-class.

'What do I remember about the journey? My foolish child, I can still smell the food. My mouth waters at the thought of it. The best food is when one is hungry, so the saying goes. I ate cabbage soup seasoned with sour cream. I feasted on black bread and herring. I had sugar to put in my tea. I sat in a carriage with soft seats and sleeping berths. The whole world was burning and I travelled first-class.

'I saw prisoners lying on platforms, chained, and in rags. By the tracks stood old babushkas dressed in black, begging for food. In the villages that flew by, I glimpsed skinny children, barefooted, running over dusty lanes, and bearded peasants bent over barren fields.

'The whole of Russia was hungry. An entire empire was searching for food. Yet in Irkutsk I bought a fish freshly caught in Lake Baikal, the best fish in the world. A giant of a fish. So soft. So thick with flesh. So well cooked. Full of juice. It was a *mekhaiye*. A pure delight. Even now, the thought of eating that fish can make my mouth drool.

'I was afraid, of course. Whenever anyone asked me about the suitcases, I would say they were not mine. My heart thumped whenever anyone passed them by. Again I had *mazel*. Every carriage had a commissar, a spy. The commissar admired my gold watch. I gave him the watch and he turned a blind eye to my luggage. When we finally reached Vladivostok he put me up in his house. He fed me well. In exchange I gave him woollen socks, warm underwear, a jar of caviar.

'We remained in Vladivostok for two weeks. It was a dump at the ends of the earth. Very few of us believed we would get out. This is what we thought, even as we boarded the boat for Japan. The ropes were untied. We moved away from the wharf. When he realised we were truly on the way, the man standing next to me started to cry. He could not believe he was free. Or perhaps he was thinking of those he had left behind. I don't know whether he was crying from happiness or pain.

'I gave him a pickled herring and a nip of vodka. We drank each other's health. We were on our way, and still, he was crying. But I was laughing. And singing. Farria. Farria. Farria. Farria. Far-ri-ya-ha-ha-ha-ha-ha.

'Yes, I was singing. And why not? My three faithful companions, the suitcases, had made it safely aboard. I ate like a king. I had dollars. I had pounds. I had diamonds. I had gefilte fish and red-berry jam. I was out on the open seas. I was safe. And I was free. My foolish child, what more can I say? The old world was burning, and I was free!'

There are languid days in our city which obliterate memory. The seas are pale, the skies bleached white, the waves enfeebled by lack of breeze. Such days numb all thoughts. The skin drips sweat and sun. All is reduced to the body.

From the concrete walk of St Kilda pier, the inner city looms close. Beyond the breakwater, pale-silver upon the horizon, curves the bridge that links the city to the west. Like a migrating bird it swoops over a distant enclave of cranes, elongated chimneys and petrochemical works.

When standing at the end of the pier Yossel feels gloved by the bay. The rocks of the breakwater are matted with moss. Boats huddle at their moorings. Two men stripped to the waist, their upper bodies ivory-white, tend their fishing lines. Ageing sunbathers sprawl on the rocks, their skin burnt a permanent bronze. A boy wades into the shallows with a dog. A young woman promenades in a bikini and heavy boots, the fashion of the day: erotic, hard-edged, casual.

Everything is casual. And slow. Heat is the leveller, reducing us all to creatures of the moment, to bodies bleached by light and sand. Yet even on days such as this Yossel clings to the past. He is nearing ninety and still he does not give in. He makes his way back to Scheherazade with steady, determined steps. He greets Avram and Masha with a wave, and sits down at his customary place.

As I approach the table Yossel is anxious, restive, twirling an ashtray, adjusting his gold bow tie, which perches on a beige shirt. His cream safari-suit matches perfectly. His gold cuff links flash under the cafe lights. And I know in advance how he will greet me:

'Sholem Aleichem!'

And I know what he will say next.

'My foolish child, age does not matter. Willpower can defeat it. I can still lift fifty kilos. I have already walked fifteen kilometres today.'

And I know that he will leap up and kiss me on both cheeks, and I will feel his vigour, laced with the scent of eau de cologne. I will smell the lingering aroma of brandy on his mouth, and he will call me his old *khaver*, his loyal friend, though I have not known him so very long. He will embrace me and exclaim, 'My dear Martin, sell your pants if you must, but nothing is worth more than a friend you can trust. Believe me. I know. I am a Krochmalna boy.'

And before I have time to respond, he will launch into an irrepressible tirade.

'My foolish child, what do you know of the past? What do you know about such things? For many it was a *tragedia*, a true hell. But for me it was not so bad. It was a lottery, whether you lived or died, whether you laughed or cried. What can I say! I had *mazel*, and I spent my war years in Shanghai.

'Of all the cities I have known, Shanghai was the best, the most beautiful. You cannot imagine it. My beloved Warsaw was burning. Krochmalna Street was circled by barbed walls. My loved ones were in *gehennim*, and in Shanghai I had a good life.

'A Yiddish life. With Yiddish theatre. First-class. With the best actors. From Warsaw and Vilna. From Odessa and Harbin. And Yiddish clubs. Yiddish radio. Yiddish newspapers: *Unzer Leben, Unzer Welt, Dos Wort* and *Der Yiddisher Almanach.*'

And the ghetto? The internment camps? The bombings?

'Of course, my dear Martin, after Pearl Harbor, it all changed. Of course we were squashed into Hongkew. Yes, it is true, we could be beaten up when we queued for a pass. Hundreds died of starvation. Of typhus. Of cholera. Of malaria and *meshugas*.

'Of course I saw the bombings. I was in the street at the time. I saw it all. I saw the planes swooping over Hongkew, and people diving into the gutters. I heard the bombs whistling as they hurtled down. I saw the corpses lying on the road, with flies crawling over their wounds. I could smell the bloated bodies in the heat. I saw people frantically searching for their loved ones. I saw dismembered coolies slumped against their mangled rickshaws. I saw it all.

'Yet somehow, for me, Shanghai was a beautiful life. That is how I remember it. What do you want me to say? That I am ashamed? That I should not have enjoyed myself when I had the chance? If not for Mao I would have stayed. Even at the worst of times I still loved it. I knew how to get by. During my six weeks, en route, in Kobe, I sold the diamonds I had smuggled from Vilna; and I arrived in Shanghai with cash in hand.

'In Shanghai there were millionaires, Sephardic Jews. Their ancestors had lived for centuries in Baghdad. They sailed to Shanghai like Sinbad of the Arabian Nights. They lived in mansions. They ran shipping lines, owned cotton mills, managed banks. They took me to nightclubs and cabarets. We drank whisky. We sipped expensive liqueurs. And all this while my Warsaw was burning. All this while my family was in *gehennim*. It's a *meshugene velt*. What can I say?

'In Shanghai there were Jews from the entire world. From Bombay. Thessaloniki, Persia and Cochin. Magnates! They owned factories, warehouses, real estate. You know why they call it 'real estate'? Because you can touch it; because it is not a fantasy, a grandmother's tale.

'I met the famous magnate, Sir Victor Sassoon, in the lobby of the Hotel Cathay. He was a great philanthropist. He walked with a limp, and he showered money on all who came!

'It was such a pleasure to stroll in the carpeted foyer. I would loiter for hours in a magnificent hall that overlooked the

Whangpoo. Even the elevators were like palace rooms. It was a delight to press the buttons, to wait for the lifts to arrive. I rode them up and down as if I was riding a horse on a carousel. I lifted my hat to the wealthy merchants who stepped in. I greeted them with a wink. A smile. And I made conversation.

'Small talk leads to big talk, to contracts and deals. This is how I met the millionaire, Baruch. His grand-daughter was Esther Williams, the actress. From Hollywood. That's what he told me. Perhaps he was just boasting. Or perhaps I have got it all mixed up.

'I met Kadourie and Hardoon. Or perhaps I heard stories about Kadourie and Hardoon. I can't remember which was which. Kadourie erected a beautiful school for refugees, where it was needed most, in that rat hole called Hongkew. He was a man with a golden heart. I am sure he sits in *gan eiden*, serenaded by angels on all sides!

'Hardoon too had a heart of gold. He had a Chinese wife. He adopted children from many lands. He built a synagogue in honour of his father, and called it the Beth Aharon, the House of Aron. And when the refugees came, he gave it to them as a gift. He opened its doors to the boys of the Mir Yeshiva. Can you imagine it? A whole yeshiva, from the Polish town of Mir, a mere shtetl, made it all the way to Shanghai.

'Yes. This is how it was! They fled from Mir to Vilna, hundreds of rabbis and yeshiva boys. They ran from Vilna to northern Lithuania where they lived secretly in villages until Chiune Sugihara helped them along. They travelled from Vilna to Vladivostok, from Kobe to Shanghai. A complete school of Talmudic studies in a caravanserai! With scholars who tugged at their side-locks, and teenage boys who scratched their itchy cheeks. They rushed about in black-brimmed hats. Their jackets flapped in the wind. Even in the summer they hurried through the streets of Hongkew in their black coats to the Beth Aharon, to study and pray.

'I prayed there too. I can still see it before my eyes. It had an arched doorway and arched windows, high white ceilings and a white dome. It looked like the great synagogues of old.

'The Russian Jews too were great philanthropists. They had lived in Shanghai for many years and they knew how to get by. My foolish child, to be able to give, you must be able to receive. This is a golden rule.

'The Russians managed nightclubs, restaurants, cinemas and cabarets. I would often stroll in the Russian quarter, along Avenue Joffre, in the French concession. Little Moscow, it was called. It was crowded with people speaking in Slavic tongues. Naturally I felt at home. I sniffed the air and soon became a regular customer at the Balalaika, the Kavkas and the Renaissance. Little Moscow was a paradise of borscht and black bread, and stores that sold everything from Siberian furs to samovars!

'The whole world was in Shanghai. *Der gantzer velt.* As Mendel Mandelbaum used to say:

> *"Die velt is ful mit veltelekh*
> *Un men shpilt zikh in beheltelekh"*

'That's how it is. The world is full of little worlds, and we are all playing hide-and-seek. This is what Mendel Mandelbaum taught me. This is what I learnt on Krochmalna Street, and in the tenement courtyards of old Warsaw. And this is why Shanghai was so familiar to me. It brought back childhood memories of peddlers selling smoked herring and bagels; and of geese and pigs being driven to market through narrow lanes. It was a wonderful mess, a *balagan*. As the boat approached the busy wharves, I rubbed my hands with glee. I fell in love at first sight. I wanted to leap into the city as soon the boat pulled up to the port.

'What can I say? In Shanghai I had a beautiful life. I lived with other single men in a dormitory, in Hongkew. Until Pearl Harbor we could roam wherever we wished. I walked the streets of the French concession, and sat in Viennese cafes. I sipped coffee with the boys from Berlin. And with the boys from Prague, Siberia and Harbin. Each group had their own cafe, their own little world. Mendel Mandelbaum was right. The whole world is full of little worlds, and we are playing hide-and-seek.

'And wherever I met people I pencilled in their names. To prosper you must have an address book with you at all times. If you wish to make a living, you must always be prepared!'

Yossel is in full flight. His gold bow tie glitters in the late afternoon light. He orders a glass of borscht. The drink complements his tales, for he is talking of Russian philanthropists. He is singing the praises of Boris Salamonik.

'My foolish child, to have money is the greatest thing. Even in times of danger some people knew how to give, how to be a *mensch,* a true human being. Boris was married to a *tsigeiner.* He helped everyone, the Gypsies, the Chinese, even the yeshiva boys from Mir. Salamonik gave them thousands of dollars to print the Talmud. They had no books for their studies, so Boris helped them.

'And he helped me. He dealt in mink. He exported it to America. The best mink. I have photos. I carry them with me in my wallet. They remind me of my luck. Look. Here is a photo of me with Boris, wrapped in his winter coat. He treated me as a son. To have money is the greatest thing. With money you can help yourself. You can help others. And Boris helped me.

'And he helped in a nice way, with honour, without making me feel like a beggar. He gave me textiles and said, "Go and deal. Go and make a living." He did not give you charity. He gave you a chance. After I made money, I too was able to help others. My foolish child, this is how it is. This is the way the world spins and turns.'

Yossel orders his customary chicken schnitzel. He eats with relish, as if each morsel could be his last.

'I did anything to survive,' he says. 'I smuggled goods, traded in diamonds, exchanged my hard-earned money on the black market. I even purchased the complete works of Karl Marx and Adam Smith from a refugee, and made a ten-fold profit by selling them for their weight! Like everything in Shanghai, paper was in demand. They had opposite views, Marx and Smith, but in weight they were worth the same!

'But unless my life depended upon it I never traded on *Shabbes*. This is where I drew the line. On Friday nights I would get dressed in my best clothes, and I would stroll to the Beth Aharon synagogue to pray. I stood at the polished pews, alongside the yeshiva boys, and rocked back and forth until I found myself in the prayer houses of old.

'After the service I would go to Goldbloom's restaurant. It was *heimish*. As homely as a mother's kitchen; and the food was kosher. Do you think it would be otherwise? We sang *zmires*, *Shabbes* songs. We drank kosher port, as if we were back on Krochmalna. We drank wine as if each *Shabbes* was a Passover feast.

'Yes, Shanghai was a *tragedia*. But we made a life. A Russian life. A French life. A Chinese life. Any life you wished. We danced to gramophones in private rooms. We went to all-night dances and ran after beautiful girls. We watched American films at the Lafayette. We saw Dorothy Lamour at the Broadway, as my beloved Warsaw fell. We watched Bette Davis at the Uptown cinema, while my dear parents perished in hell.

'Of course, the situation changed after December '41. Of course the party was over. But even then, in Hongkew, there were coffee-houses; they multiplied like flies. We had little food. We drank ersatz coffee. We ate soggy rice drowning in water. We ate red beans until we burst; but we could breathe! We sat for hours on end and shuffled cards. We played ping-pong and dribbled footballs in rubbish-strewn lots. We sat with coolies and played mahjong. What else could we do but live for the day?

'In Hongkew lovers grappled in each other's arms in dark corners and lanes. I saw them with my own eyes. My foolish child! What can you know of such things? Even in a slum, the spirit thrives.

'And compared with those who stayed behind we were in paradise. Ah, now that was a true *tragedia*. What happened to us was nothing in comparison. *Gornisht*. At least we had a tiny bit of room in which to move. At least we could have affairs, bear children, and bury our dead, the way they should be buried, with a tombstone to mark their names. At least we could drink coffee as the rest of the world burned. Perhaps that is why I loved it. Perhaps that is why I still dream of Shanghai. In Shanghai I survived!'

As I leave the cafe I feel disoriented. The footpath seems malleable under foot. Nothing feels certain. Yet everything appears vibrant, ablaze. The Europa cake shop glistens with sugar-coated dreams of a distant past: sacher rum and cherry kougelhupf. Vanilla knipfel and almond horseshoe. Baked cheesecake, Vienna rings, hazelnut meringues and honey sponge.

I catch a tram and find relief in the breeze that flows through its open doors. The Upper Esplanade is lined with luxury apartments and dishevelled hotels. The sea is a scorching silver that scalds the eyes. A haze sinks from low-hung skies. A solitary ship crawls across the bay. The green-domed clocktower marks the passing of a summer day.

The tram curves into Fitzroy Street. Ageing elm trees line the way. Tables sprawl at kerbside cafes. Pimps and prostitutes survey their domain. Backpackers finger their copies of *The World on Twenty Dollars a Day*. It is shabby, yet somehow it seems new. A world of sojourners and itinerants, unhinged and unearthed.

I too have become a walker, a cafe dweller. I too have become unhinged, so taken by Laizer, Zalman and Yossel's stories that all I see about me seems like a parade, a play of chance.

'We are *luftmenschen*,' is how Yossel put it, with a laugh. 'People of air. We do not belong to any one place. The whole world is ours. Yet, despite all our running about, nothing is truly ours. My foolish child, this is how it is.'

VII

Walk the familiar route. The inner city is coated in dew. St Kilda pier is lined with lamps that glow like miniature moons. A woman leans across the rails. A couple embrace on the deserted beach, a middle-aged man slumps back on a wooden seat. The Palais Theatre rears like a Gothic castle in the mist.

Walk the streets of Shanghai; walk the lanes of Krochmalna; walk the crumbling courtyards of Vilna; the foothills of Kobe; walk the ancient trading route. Walk the pier. Walk the pavement. Walk the shoreline of the bay. Walk and come to know that others have walked here for millennia. Walk the contours, the flatlands, the hills, the rivers and creeks coursing like arteries to the bay. Walk and come to know that this land abounds in tales, both ancient and new.

Retrace your steps along the familiar route. Observe the neon sign coming into view, Scheherazade blinking lilac, pink and blue. Proceed through the glass doors. Make your way past the front alcove where the boys are playing cards. Move past the men immersed in journals and racing guides. Sidestep the tables where families are gulping down their meals; and make your way to the back room.

They are there, as usual, Mr and Mrs Zeleznikow, Avram

and Masha, the proprietors, in their directors' chairs, issuing orders, poring over bills, shuffling papers, reading the news.

So join us, dear reader. Don't be shy. Here, have a slice of Black Forest cake. On the house. And a glass of red. Savour it. Feel the glow spreading over your cheeks. Allow the taste to linger in the mouth. It is a pleasant feeling, no? Are you comfortable? Sit back. Settle into your chair; and listen to *bobbe mayses,* grandma tales:

> Listen to this story children,
> Listen with nose and eyes.
> Over grandma's house
> A cow I saw did fly.
> This is true, this is true,
> This is true, it all took place.
> This is true, this is true,
> This indeed, I saw myself.

The war is over. Empires lie in ruins. A weariness has descended upon the world. Travellers trudge across the horizon clad in rags. They sleep in barns, abandoned cottages, burnt-out buildings. They emerge from temporary refuges, remote hamlets. They disperse from disbanding armies and the labour camps of the east. It is time to seek out the loved ones they have left behind. It is time to journey home.

Masha's family were among the first to return to Poland. In September 1945, the Frydmans boarded a train in Dzhambul.

Cold winds penetrated the wagons. The early snows were falling. Tall grasses bent to a bitter breeze. Forests vanished into the shadows. Villages receded in huddles of light.

They travelled in silence. All about them they saw others on the move; on the backs of trucks, in bare feet, on bicycles and horse-drawn carts; they moved like weary battalions in quiet retreat. They travelled towards a land shrouded in rumours. They prayed that their loved ones had survived. They were afraid of what they would find.

Yet nothing could have prepared them for the devastation that had been wrought in their absence: the piles of rubble, twisted girders, the razed hamlets, the wastelands of defeat. Nothing could have readied them for the scorched earth, the ruined cities, the desecrated temples and shattered homes.

This is when their stories began to be suppressed. This is when the Frydmans, and so many others who had survived in the east, were overwhelmed by the demands of others in far greater distress; and by an urgent need to forget, to bury the past and to rebuild their aborted lives.

'When we first met,' says Masha, 'Avram told me that all those years in *gehennim* he had dreamt of a white room. A brightly lit room. With a desk at which he could sit and write. That is all he wanted, a room with an electric light.'

'I dreamt about it all the time,' says Avram, 'in all those years of crawling through swamps and shit, I dreamt of a white room.

With a desk at which I could sit and record my days in the Kingdom of Night.'

'When we first met, I fell in love with his stories. He made me feel I had led a sheltered life. He made me feel I had nothing to complain about. Avram's stories made me feel that my suffering had been trivial.'

'We met at a Bund gathering. In the Polish countryside, near Wroclaw. In the summer of 1946. I was twenty-two, and Masha was nineteen. For me it was love at first sight.'

'I was not so sure. I could see he was not ambitious. I could see he was a dreamer. All he wanted was a white room, with a desk, and a light. Can you believe it? That I fell in love with his stories?'

'I thought we could rebuild our lives in Poland,' says Avram. 'I travelled the countryside on Bund missions. I collected children from hiding, from convents and nunneries, from cellars, attics and warrens dug deep in the ground. I retrieved them from peasants who had concealed them behind false walls. And I collected documents for our archives. I was driven by a need to record, to pick up the pieces, to reconnect. But inside I felt empty. I had a craving for human touch, a welcoming face.'

'I sensed it in him from the beginning,' says Masha, 'his need to be heard; and it frightened me. Yet it drew me to him. At the same time I was anxious to get on with my own life. I was nineteen and full of hopes. I did not want to be like my mother, a servant of the family. I wanted to study, to fend for myself.'

'I wanted to remake my life,' says Avram. 'I wanted to

restore the Jewish communities of Poland. I settled in Lodz. I became active in the Bund. We tried to help those who survived. We welcomed refugees, found them a place to stay, and tried to determine the fate of their loved ones. And I loved Lodz. Compared to my devastated Vilna, it was beautiful.'

'I wanted to study medicine. I moved from Katowice, where my parents had resettled, to Lodz. I enrolled in the university. From all over Poland they were returning. From camps, from forests and hiding places. Each one had a story to tell. We were overwhelmed by their tales. I was overwhelmed by Avram. I had a mother, a father, a brother, a sister, all of whom were alive. We had all survived, but Avram was completely alone.'

'At that time,' says Avram, 'I read a book that seemed to reflect my situation. We all read this book. *Arc de Triomphe,* it was called. Written by Erich Maria Remarque, a German writer, the very same author who wrote *All Quiet on the Western Front.* It was a book about stateless people. A book about lovers. A book about us. And it was in this book that we first heard of a nightclub called Scheherazade.'

'Avramel, you should explain that Scheherazade was in Paris. A cabaret where Russian emigres would meet, where they felt at home. This was where they heard the music of their past, played on Gypsy violins. Where they talked and reminisced, and imagined the day of their return. And this was where Remarque's lovers met, the doctor and the cabaret singer. Whenever they met, they would drink an apple brandy called Calvados.'

'When I read this book,' says Avram, 'I began, for the first time, to dream of Paris, of other cities, other worlds. When I read this book I began to imagine a different way of living, a new life.'

'Avramel, you are jumping ahead again. You have not told Martin the full story—the stories that so overwhelmed me, and made mine seem so mild, the stories that I could hardly believe when I first heard them, and that still fill me with wonder and disbelief. You have not told him about the Kingdom of Night.'

It was twilight in the Jerusalem of eastern Europe, a lull before the final storm. It broke on a sunlit Sunday morning, 22 June 1941. They came from the west, in waves. They darkened the Vilna skies. They heralded a reign of terror. They unleashed a hail of bombs that pounded the heart of the city.

The Red Army scattered towards the east. Within two days the Nazis entered the city gates. Mobs rampaged through the streets. Homes were looted and plundered. Jewish men between the ages of sixteen and sixty-five were rounded up and thrown onto trucks that conveyed them to the forests of Ponary, a village eight kilometres from the city. They were ordered to strip naked, lined up side by side, and shot into mass graves. Body piled upon body. The freshly dug earth was tossed onto the bodies, both dead and alive.

As the assault raged with increasing ferocity, Avram

remained hidden within the walls of the family home. He stayed put in the beloved city. He hid in the darkness. He had entered the Kingdom of Night.

Avram has told the tale many times. He is an avid guardian of the past. He tells it as a sacred duty. He tells it with restraint. Yet with each telling it retains its power to astonish.

He remained hidden for days. He finally stole out of Vilna at night. He walked forest paths to the village of Resze, twenty-five kilometres distant. On the outskirts of the village there stood a peat works. By day Avram would trudge to the swamps to extract peat from the rotting earth. In the evenings he returned to the factory barracks, where he would hear the most recent rumours, the latest report.

With each passing night, the news was more frightening. His loved ones were forbidden to walk on the Vilna footpaths. They were forced to crawl in the gutters. They were ordered to wear yellow stars on their shirts. Menfolk were seized at night, and driven out of their homes. They left carrying towels and soap, and vanished into the forests of Ponary. For six weeks the assault continued. Peasants who had witnessed the mass shootings confirmed the rumours. Ponary had become a killing field.

In the final days of August, the Lithuanian manager of the peat works returned to Resze from Vilna and warned his workers that the Nazis were planning a massive pogrom. He had reliable contacts. It would take place in early September. Avram sent a message to Vilna, via a Polish peasant. He delivered the letter to the family home, urging his loved ones to escape.

The peasant returned with Avram's sister Basia, her husband Uri, and their six-year-old son Shmulek. But his mother, Etta, refused to leave. She was done with furtive journeys. After so many years on the run she had made a life in Vilna, and created the stable home she always craved.

On 6 September 1941 the foundation she had built was torn from beneath her feet. The Jews of Vilna were driven from their dwellings. They were herded into two ghettos. Those with trades, skills, those deemed useful, ripe for slavery, were assembled in the first ghetto. The weak, the old, the expendable were herded into the second.

When Avram heard the news he persuaded his boss to provide him with a horse and wagon. Disguised as a peasant he drove to Vilna with a load of peat. He delivered the peat and drove to the family home. When he saw Avram at the door, the Polish janitor was terrified. He crossed himself repeatedly. Etta had been taken to the second ghetto, which was located in the old Jewish quarter of Vilna.

He had lost all fear, Avram tells me, as if still in awe at the fact. He had entered another state of being where all calculation ceased. He drove openly through Vilna's streets. He urged his horse through the ghetto gates under the noses of armed guards. He located his mother and two elderly friends in the attic of a three-storey tenement. They had not eaten for a week.

Again Etta refused to leave for Resze. She preferred to move to the first ghetto, where she could join her friends and comrades. Avram guided her down the stairs, lifted her onto the wagon and, with the same audacity with which he had entered, he escorted her out into the open streets, and back through the gates of the first ghetto.

Avram returned to Resze by nightfall. He brought back letters and news to fellow workers who still had family in the city. Reports of mass killings continued to reach them day after day. Within weeks Avram embarked on a second peat run. As he drove towards the ghetto entrance he saw a crowd of inmates being led out. Among them walked his mother.

Avram drove the horse into the crowd. He beat back the guards, and dragged his mother onto the wagon. Passers-by could not believe what was happening in front of their eyes. It was his audacity that enabled him to get away with it. He drove through the city in a trance. His life had become a trance. And it is in a trance that he continues the story, at a table in the back room of Scheherazade.

Avram returned to Resze. Etta was reunited with her daughter and grandchild. It did not last long, this sojourn in the forests. The factory manager had received news of an impending raid. The Nazis had learnt that Jews were hiding in the peat works.

The Zeleznikows made their way back to the city. They stole into the first ghetto. Only those who possessed a yellow work pass could remain. The others hid. If discovered they would be rounded up and led to their deaths. Only slaves were permitted to exist.

Uri obtained work in the ghetto kitchen. This entitled him to register Basia and Shmulek. On Yom Kippur, the Day of Atonement, 1941, those who did not possess yellow passes were ordered to assemble in the streets. Etta was smuggled into the kitchen where her son-in-law worked. Avram clambered onto the roof and hid in an attic chimney. An elderly Jew tried to follow him. He was spotted by a Lithuanian policeman. Both Avram and the elderly Jew were dragged from the chimney, and driven down several flights of stairs to the street.

Avram was now covered in blood and soot. He tried to disappear into a crowd of workers who had yellow passes. The chief of the Jewish ghetto police, Jacob Gens, dragged him out and handed him over to German officers. Avram was among the thousands who were herded into the second ghetto.

The centuries-old Jewish quarters of Vilna were in ruins. The renowned synagogue had been reduced to rubble. The second ghetto had been liquidated. Shredded bedding and clothes, photo albums and dismembered dolls, charred shards of glass, lay scattered in smouldering homes. The building which had housed Wolfke's was one of the many that were gutted. The courtyard of the Sage of Vilna was no more. And those assembled in its ruins knew, with helpless certainty, that before them lay one final journey, to the killing fields of Ponary.

Avram seized his last chance. A pre-war friend, Dr Anatolski, and a group of nurses, had been allowed into the second ghetto to tend to the wounded. Avram appealed to him for help. Anatolski allowed Avram to crouch beneath a stretcher.

Barely concealed, Avram walked, like a dog, back into the first ghetto, while those who were left behind perished, just hours later, in what was to become known as the 'Yellow Pass *Aktions*'.

Again I observe Avram's hands. They possess a language of their own. He inscribes ever-widening circles. The circles indicate a vastness, an incomprehension. His clenched fists are clenched emotions. They precede the most searing of memories. A story almost impossible to tell. A story we wish to avoid, both teller and listener.

There was something else about that night of the Yellow Pass *Aktions*, on Yom Kippur, 1941. The inmates had been driven to the ghetto gates. Alsatians howled and tore at their feet. SS men and camp guards wielded rifle butts and bayonets. Gestapo officers sat at wooden tables where they processed every man, woman and child.

Each adult with work passes was to be allowed three names on their yellow pass: one member of the opposite sex, and two children. Any children in excess would be taken. The decision had to be made within seconds. Those with more than two children had to choose who they would keep, who they would abandon. If no choice were made, they would all perish in the forests of Ponary.

Avram heard the screams from his place of hiding. Tears come to his eyes in the telling. Tears come to my eyes in the listening. We are descending, Avram and I, in the back room of the cafe. We are moving together. Step by step. Each step is another realm. A step closer to an unfathomable darkness.

Avram clenches his fists tighter. The chairs seem to career across the polished floors. The cafe walls close in around us. Those seated at nearby tables evaporate into ghosts. Neon-lit Acland Street recedes. The city we inhabit whirls about us. And again we are elsewhere, by the gates of the ghetto, in the Jerusalem of eastern Europe. Children are being wrenched from their mothers. From their trusted fathers.

'Many parents were driven to insanity that night,' Avram whispers. 'We thought we were immune to tragedy. We were prepared for the worst. But not for this. It was impossible to understand. It can never be understood. Those parents who survived this *Aktion* would never forgive themselves.

'And the worst thing,' adds Avram, 'was that the perpetrators of these crimes seemed to enjoy it.'

They can come in any season. Mostly they appear in early spring, days of gale-force winds. They rise in the south, partnered by clouds borne upon sudden gusts. The bay bursts from its confines. The spray whips the eyes. The city vanishes under low-flung skies. High seas lash the pier. Boats in the marina tear at their chains. The palms on the foreshore sway, as if about to snap.

It is invigorating, this southern rage. It clears my mind. It penetrates my bones. My face feels cold and alive, my eyes clear and alert. I scan the unkempt sea, the cloud-black skies. I notice, for the first time, that there are trees, permanently bent away from the sea, beaten back, over the years, by countless southern storms. Crows and gulls spiral against the wind. Squalls hurl water onto the foreshore. The beaches are strewn with kelp flung against the retaining walls.

Never before have I so enjoyed the ferocity of a storm. It is a relief to be outside, to cling to the bay, and wander the streets. And it is a relief to be free for a while of that story-drenched cafe so burdened by the past.

But now that we have begun, we must see it through. I return, and Avram resumes his tale. Fifteen thousand inmates remain in the first ghetto. The Third Reich is in need of slaves. Avram works in an electricity plant. He leaves the ghetto at dawn, and returns from the factory at night.

The incarcerated slaves regroup. They set up schools, a kindergarten, a wall bulletin, a bookstore. A resistance movement is formed in the early days of 1942. Yitzkhak Wittenberg is elected leader. The two battalions are broken down into chapters. Each chapter is divided into cells. Avram becomes chairman of the ghetto youth club. The club produces exhibitions and plays. They smuggle in weapons and secretly train.

Houses of worship are relocated underground. Avram's sister, Basia, teaches music to ghetto children. She is one of many inmates who continue to give of their hearts and skills. Cabarets and choirs, a theatre, an orchestra, soften the despair.

Writers pour their suffering into laments and dirges. Haunting melodies rise from the ashes. A poet roams the ghetto alleys in a vain search for his vanished lover:

> Springtime, take away my sadness,
> Restore my dear one to me again.
> Oh springtime, take away my sadness,
> Convey my sweetheart back to me again.

His name is Shmerl Katcherginsky. Or Shmerke as he is affectionately known. His songs mirror the feelings of his people, his fellow inmates. They recite his poems, they whisper his songs and, for a brief moment, they are comforted:

> Hush, be silent, remain silent,
> Corpses are growing here.
> They were sown by men of evil,
> Raised from seeds of fear.
> There are paths to Ponary,
> But none that lead away.
> Oh, our father has been lost,
> Our loved ones wrapped in clay.
> Hush my child, weep not my love,
> Our cry will not be heard;
> Quiet my child, sleep my treasure
> Your tears, they fall in vain.
> Only when our freedom returns
> Will its light wash away your pain.

The end looms in the Jerusalem of Lithuania, yet there are those who bear children, a crime punishable by death. Basia gives birth to her second child in a concealed room within the ghetto hospital. She names her Nehamiah, the Hebrew word for 'hope'. She retreats to the windowless room in which she lives with Etta and Avram, her husband Uri, and little Shmulek.

Nehamiah is not yet four months old when, on 5 July 1943, Yitzkhak Wittenberg is arrested. As he is being led from the ghetto, those guarding him are attacked and killed. The Gestapo issues an ultimatum: if Wittenberg does not surrender by morning, the ghetto will be liquidated.

After an agonising night, Wittenberg complies. Several units of ghetto fighters decide to make a run for the forest. They are ambushed en route. Many die in the subsequent battle. In reprisal the Nazis murder the families and workmates of the escapees.

On 1 September 1943, the ghetto is sealed off. In the following weeks thousands are herded towards the Vilna station. Those still capable of work are transported to labour camps: the men to Estonia, the women to Latvia. The old, the sick, the lame, the remaining women and children, all those deemed not fit for slave labour, are trucked out to be shot in Ponary, or entrained to the gas chambers of Majdanek. The final liquidation of Vilna ghetto has begun.

Avram and his comrades retreat to a courtyard beside the ghetto library on Strashuna Street. Its precious collection of books is torn from the shelves and thrown onto the barricades, alongside pieces of metal, furniture, bedding and bricks. After the initial shoot-out the Nazis retreat; but the deportations continue.

The decision is finally made by the partisan command. The ghetto fighters are to steal out to the forests. An uprising within the ghetto walls would be of no avail. Better to continue the resistance underground.

In the early hours of 23 September, Avram and his comrades leave the library, and descend into Strashuna Street. At first light Avram comes across his mother, by chance. He has not seen her for six weeks. She is hurrying by with Basia who holds baby Nehamiah in her arms. Little Shmulek clutches her other hand.

'She knew it was the end,' says Avram. 'I gave her some bread and milk for the baby, and she gave me the scarf she was wearing. She wanted me to be warm. "Take care of yourself in the forest," she told me. Those were her final words.'

It would remain the most indelible image, the sight of his family vanishing through the smoke and rubble, in the first light of day. It continues to haunt Avram, this final glimpse of Basia, Shmulek, baby Nehamiah, and his mother, the lifelong revolutionary, moving away to certain death. His mother's words still pursue him. The memory will follow him to the grave.

Avram leans back against his chair. His coffee has turned cold. His feet are drawn up to the side. His face is tense, the colour drained. He is like a child cowering, withdrawing into himself. 'Have I told you this story?' he asks.

166

'In the ghetto there was a yeshiva for young boys. The head of the yeshiva was a cabbalist, a student of Jewish mysticism, a numerologist who believed that the universe had a mathematical perfection. He had an uncanny ability to use his knowledge of numbers to make accurate predictions. Even in the ghetto, he would immerse himself in the *Zohar*, the Book of Radiance, the great text of the cabbalists. He loved his God and worshipped him day and night; and he loved his boys as much as he loved his God.

'In the final days of the liquidation the boys were flushed from the cellar in which they were hiding, and driven out to Ponary. When he discovered his students' fate, the *rosh yeshiva* lost his mind. He ran through the streets of the ghetto screaming: "*Yidn*, there is no God. Do not believe it. No God would allow this to happen. *Yidn*, it is a lie. There cannot be a God!"

'We could hear his screams from our barricades. "*Yidn*, they have murdered my boys. *Yidn*, there is no God. No God would allow this to happen!" For hours he ran, screaming the same words, like a man possessed; he did not stop screaming until he too was shot.'

Avram pauses. His knees are bent back, held tight. He leans to the side and clutches his chair. His face is white, his body contorted. Around us the hum of conversation continues. It is as if our table has been cordoned off.

When Avram's voice returns, it arises as a whisper. Like a child awoken from a disturbing dream, he asks, 'Now tell me, how can anyone emerge from such a place without rage? Tell me, how could anyone emerge from all this and remain sane?'

The city is burning. The ancient walls are crumbling. The air is rent with the barking of dogs, the moans of the wounded. Avram and his comrades enter the sewers. He clutches a 14mm Colt revolver and four bullets, his ration of firepower. Urine drips from the walls. The tunnels narrow to half a metre in width. A comrade faints at the smell of stale air and shit.

From the distance can be heard the sound of shots. The tunnel reverberates with the aftershock. Five partisans who had preceded them have been discovered. They are dragged out and hanged in Subosz Square, in front of a crowd of ghetto inmates.

Among the executed are Avram's close friends, Abraham Cwornik and Ashia Bik. That morning Avram had come across them making love on the floor of the barricaded library. They lay on a bed of books, and sought to enter each other, oblivious to their surroundings. He was in his forties. She was twenty-one. They made love in the morning, and they were hanged in the afternoon, side by side.

Avram and his comrades emerged from the sewers at night. They were met by contacts who guided them to a fur factory. Two days later they were transferred from the factory to Gestapo headquarters on Slovacki Street.

It was an audacious move. The Lithuanian concierge hid them in the attic. They remained there for three nights, awaiting their contacts in the forests. Below them they heard the voices and movements of Gestapo officers. They were in the belly of the beast.

'Fear is a feeling one has when there are choices,' says Avram. 'We had no choice. We wanted to survive. Perhaps this is what is called the preservation instinct. Fear is paralysing.

'Only years later did I feel it again, here, in Melbourne, when my son contracted polio. Until then I had remained immune to fear. All I felt was the desire for revenge, fuelled by a rage I found impossible to tame. But when I had children, a family of my own, and I saw the agony of my own son, I began to feel afraid. I wanted him to be well. I did not want to see him suffer.'

As he talks I see in him the nineteen-year-old youth, emerging from the sewers, hiding in Gestapo headquarters, stealing out to the forests. I see the ghetto fighter. I sense the residual anger. And I am struck by the contrast: between Avram's tales, and the setting in which he tells them; between the images of old Vilna, disintegrating into dust, and the intimacy of Scheherazade on a cold spring night.

'Sholem Aleichem.'

'Aleichem Sholem.'

'Here. Take a seat. What do you wish to order? A glass of borscht? Some barley soup?

'You speak a word of Yiddish? *Mamme loschen*? A little

Russian? Maybe Polish? What do you want for the main course? A plate of latkes? A chicken schnitzel or vegetable stew?

'And where are you from? Warsaw? Budapest? Crakow? Lublin? Perhaps Vienna? Maybe Berlin? And what would you like for dessert? An apple compote? A plate of cheese? A cup of coffee? A lemon tea?'

'This is how it started to become the Scheherazade we know today,' Masha tells me.

'We could not foresee what it would become,' says Avram.

'We had no experience,' adds Masha. 'We had never been restaurateurs, chefs, business people, when we took over O'Shea's milk bar.'

'Then the single men began to come, men who had lost their entire families in the Annihilation, some of whom had never remarried,' says Avram. 'Men who lived in one-bedroom flats, boarding houses, single rooms. And we responded to their tastes.'

The word spread. The men gathered. Scheherazade answered their needs. Their numbers grew like a sprouting of seeds. They came in search of a Yiddish word, a familiar smile. This is what the survivors craved: a mother's touch, a friend's embrace.

Their longings determined Masha's cuisine. Slowly it returned, her recall of recipes, the ingredients she had helped her mother prepare on a wood-fuelled fire in a Siberian camp.

It began with simple dishes: a chicken broth, a Sabbath stew. The menu expanded. The clientele grew. Masha dashed between tables. She ran upstairs to tend to her three children. She ran downstairs to tend to her family of solitary men. Avram settled accounts, paid bills, dashed to communal meetings, and rushed back in time to serve supper, sweep the floors, lower the shutters and bolt the doors.

Masha had wanted to be a doctor. She wanted to pursue the future she had envisaged on her walks to a village school through the dust-clogged alleys of Merke. Avram had wanted to teach, to seek answers, to record his precious tales; but when they arrived in Melbourne, they had to begin anew. They laboured in clothing factories. They advanced from a stint in a laundry and an abattoir, to late-night piecework and assembly lines; until they laid their eyes upon O'Shea's.

The milk bar became a coffee shop, the coffee shop a restaurant, the restaurant a meeting place, a refuge from the cold. In Scheherazade survivors were regrouping, old worlds were being recreated, and festering wounds were being healed. Yet it would take the proprietors years to see the poetry of their venture.

Avram and his comrades retreated to the forests. They moved to an island in the Rudnicki swamps. They dug *zemlankes*, underground rooms, camouflaged with branches and leaves.

The shelters expanded. Avram and his comrades added a kitchen, a bakery and a sauna: a row of stones fuelled by burning wood. The steam provided relief from armies of lice, and drove them from their breeding grounds in shirts and matted hair. The partisans drew water from underground springs. The hot stones heated the water into warm baths.

They assembled an arsenal, and a radio by which they received orders from central command. They waded through the swamps, on makeshift walkways, made out of branches and sand. They moved to enemy lines in small bands along forest tracks. They laid mines. They blew up railway tracks. They cut down telegraph poles. They raided farmhouses, stole food and interrogated peasants. They became hardened fighters, men and women with their childhood barely behind them.

Avram recalls his initiation, the first assignment. They waded out of the swamps in the pre-dawn darkness, in the winter of 1943, a band of partisans fifteen strong, led by Rushke Markowitz. She was twenty-two years old. They made their way to a rail siding. German guards spotted them as they moved across the tracks. Rushke and a comrade diverted the guards with their fire. The rest of the band retreated as Rushke and her partner were killed.

In time, they became ruthless. There was a village of oxen and geese, and fowls squawking in the dust; with thatched cottages, wooden stables and horse-drawn carts. Its children played in windswept lanes. Its women tended their homes; its menfolk farmed. And stored arms which they used against both the German occupiers and Soviet-led partisans. The village stood on the edge of the forest. Partisans often passed nearby, to and from their raids. When they strayed too close, they were attacked, and some were killed.

The order came from Moscow. The villagers were to be taught a lesson. A combined force of partisans was assembled, comprised of Russians and Poles, Lithuanians and Jews. They ringed the entire village. They blocked all escape routes.

They attacked at midnight. They set fire to the houses, the wagons, the fences and stables. The howl of burning animals rose above the crackle of bullets and flames. Horses, with manes ablaze, hurtled towards watering holes. The madness was contagious. The hunted had become the hunter.

Placid family men became indiscriminate killers. Once pious scholars bellowed for revenge. Boys screamed out the names of loved ones as they beat their captives to death. Partisan women became oblivious to the cries of children in the glow of lingering flames. Long before the darkness had given way to the dawn, not one village man, woman or child remained alive.

Again I hear the steel in Avram's voice. I see the young man of the swamps, smeared with mud and sweat. I hear the tale, and I cannot move. All I can do is listen at the table in the back room, and allow the story to be told.

There were moments, however few, of respite. They would sit by a fire, and inhale the conifer-scented night. 'After three years of powerlessness, we could decide our own fate,' says Avram. 'We were no longer helpless. We faced death with every step, but we had a measure of control over our lives.

'And there were the hours by the fire, after a successful raid. We baked potatoes. We gazed at the glowing embers and flames. We sang Russian and Yiddish songs. We recalled fragments of our past lives and, to this day, when we meet, those who survived, those of us who settled in Melbourne or New York, in Jerusalem, Buenos Aires, Mexico City or Montreal, in cities scattered throughout the world, we feel a bond of love; and the scent of the past returns.

'In the swamps and forests we were kings. We lived by our instincts and wits. When the Luftwaffe planes circled overhead we would hide in the mud. They were too frightened to come by land. We could remain invisible in the swamps for hours on end. We ate the grass and drank our own urine to ease our thirst. We learnt that everything can be turned to an advantage. When the planes dropped their bombs, they would get stuck in the mud. We would creep up, defuse them, take out the explosives, and use them in our mines.'

As Avram speaks I see a radiance, born of freedom, of being able to defend oneself. I see him with his companions, seated on forest floors knotted with pine needles and cones. I hear the notes of a mouth organ, the chorus of a partisan song. I inhale the aroma of birches grazed with smoke. And I sense the ambiguities, the interplay of shadow and light.

As if he has intuited my thoughts, Avram adds, 'In the forests we were like eagles. There were times when we could soar. But like eagles, to survive, we had to descend back to the mud, to the smell of death, and learn to stalk our prey. We had no option but to lower ourselves in the dirt in order to regain our wings.'

Yet it could steal upon them any time: an aching sense of loss. During a raid, or as they went about their daily work, such emotions had to be suppressed. They could cause a lapse in judgment, a miscalculation at a vital moment. They could cost a comrade's life. This longing would steal upon them, nevertheless. Even as they slept, it would enter their dreams in the form of a loved one: a mother, father, husband, wife, a lover or child.

So intense were these images the dreamers did not want to wake. They reached out to touch the mirage, but found themselves back in their underground shelters, buried beneath the earth. And there were those times late at night by a dying fire, when they allowed themselves to summon a loved one's face in the glow of the embers. Or their image would be conjured up by a song:

> The flame in the hearth flickers,
> The sap on the pine flows like tears.
> The accordion is singing to me
> The song of the smile in your eyes.
> You are far from me, so very far;
> Between us stretch forests and fields,
> Between us the distance is vast.
> Yet, death is so very near.
> Sing, my accordion,
> Sing and defy the wind,

My twisted fate please unravel
And its meaning, I beg you, make clear.

Even as Avram listened to this most loved of Russian partisan songs, even as he looked about him and saw the tears in his comrades' eyes, and heard the hissing of the dying flames; even then, a future battle line was being drawn; between love and rage; between the desire to receive a lover's warmth, and the impulse to recoil; between a belief in life and a loss of faith. It was to become his greatest struggle, and it would truly begin only when the fighting was fully done.

In the first week of July 1944, Radio Moscow echoed in the Rudnicki swamps with orders from central command: abandon the forests! Pursue the retreating enemy! Join the Red Army advance!

The partisans trekked towards Vilna. As they moved through the Ponary woods, past the sites of the killing fields, they came across a freshly dug grave. Avram can still see it, the earth heaving, the grains of dirt sliding down the mounds. The final massacre had taken place just hours before their arrival. While they retreated, German soldiers had murdered sixty Polish priests.

A pall of crimson hung over the ancient city. Red Army tanks led the assault. Artillery battered the walls. A hunger for revenge seethed in the partisan ranks. For five days the battle raged over the paved streets and cobblestone lanes, from house to house, building to building, through charred courtyards and vacant lots. German soldiers and collaborators were rounded up and shot. Vilna shook under the onslaught.

Then it was over. An eerie stillness prevailed. The partisans marched through desolate streets. They wept for the loss of their loved ones. They spat on the graves of their enemies; and they lamented the beloved city that had been laid to waste.

This would be the worst night for Avram, the night of his liberation. His battalion was billeted in 'Napoleon's palace', a Vilna landmark, said to have gained its name in 1812 during his ill-fated Russian campaign. The partisans were issued with new boots, several hundred roubles, and discharged by the army command. Avram's comrades dispersed throughout the city to rejoin surviving family and friends. Avram remained in the palace. There was no one to seek out.

He paced the corridors, the palatial suites. He stood on the balconies and gazed at bombed-out streets. And the darkness claimed him. For the first time in his life, he was completely alone. He was free. The war seemed over. But he was not yet saved. His entire family had vanished into unmarked graves.

He did not know what to do with himself. He could not rest. He could not bear his solitude. He wandered the rooms with mounting panic. On the night of his liberation something seemed to give way within him: the will to live. There was no past and no future. All that he had once held so dear seemed to have been unmasked as a cruel lie.

Vilna had become a netherworld, caught between the living and the newly dead, a world of transmigrating souls. Avram surrendered to events that appeared to be beyond his control. He seethed with a sense of loss, and an overwhelming desire for vengeance. He dreamt of confronting his tormentors, the murderers of his loved ones. He imagined tearing them limb from limb, setting fire to their homes, their villages, their prized possessions. He dreamt of watching them as the terror rose in their eyes.

Yet there were times when even this one remaining desire was replaced by fatigue. 'I had seen too much brutality, too much killing,' says Avram. 'I could not take it any longer. All I wanted was to forget. But it was still taking place. Even now, on the streets of Vilna, I could not avoid it. I was part of it. The war had not truly ended. There were times when we believed it would never end.

'When I had entered Vilna with the Red Army, I came across the body of one of my former teachers, Opeshkin was his name. He was one of my childhood heroes. He had a passion for knowledge, a love of language and literature.

'He too had come out into the forests. He had fought with both weapons and words. He composed poems that depicted our plight. When we found him, his body was still warm. We had arrived just half an hour too late. I felt impotent. Life seemed to be a mere game of chance.'

Again the stories are cascading, as we move with Avram through the ruins of Vilna, seeking out informers, dragging them from their places of hiding.

'We came upon a former inmate of the ghetto, who had collaborated with the Gestapo. He hailed us as liberators. When he saw that we were going to execute him, he fell to his knees and begged for his life. His wife was screaming. She sank to her knees beside him. I tried to stop my comrades, but they were too hardened. And I was tired. So tired.

'He was sentenced to immediate death. "Killing him is not enough," said one the partisans. He took out a knife and slowly began to cut into his flesh. We had to drag him away from the screaming prisoner. A comrade took out a pistol and shot the informer on the spot. It was an act of kindness. Otherwise he would have been torn to pieces.

'The act of killing, I could not take it any more. I suppressed my feelings. I had no choice. I would have been crushed. Many times I just wanted to lie down and close my eyes. It was a sweet thought. I wanted to be rid of all feeling.'

Avram's life hung in the balance. The world was precariously poised. The Red Army was on the advance. The front was moving westwards. Vaselenko, a former comrade and partisan commander, took Avram under his wing. As the new director of railways in the Vilna district, he was anxious to secure able workers. Avram was put in charge of trains that delivered arms and food supplies to the front.

Avram pursued the job with characteristic zeal, and a sense of abandon. He no longer cared. His survival instincts had deserted him. One morning it was reported that someone had raided a shipment of vodka. While he investigated the report, a Red Army officer approached and asked for several bottles of the prized spirits. Avram refused, pulled out a revolver, and threatened to shoot if the officer disobeyed his orders.

That evening Avram was summoned to the office of the Red Army captain in charge of the station. 'Is it true that you threatened one of my men?' the captain asked. Avram did not deny the charge. The offending officer was called into the room; and again Avram refused his demands for vodka, even though they were supported by the station master.

'They could not believe I wasn't corrupt,' says Avram. 'They searched my room and my few belongings. They could not find even one bottle. They were angry. And they saw I was a fool. I did not know how to play their system. Take a bit, give a bit, make a bit on the side, and get drunk. Those were the unspoken rules of the game.'

There was something else they could not fathom. Something that is evident even now, half a century later, in the tone of voice with which Avram recounts the tale. They could not see that his zeal was the final bastion of his crumbling faith, an attempt to resurrect a shattered will.

Avram lost the job; and drifted into another, more suited to a man who had lost his capacity to feel. He was assigned to a Red Army intelligence unit. His unit was sent to the Prussian border, to newly captured territory in the wake of the army's advance. Avram interrogated those suspected of collaboration.

He knew his job well. He had practised the primitive art of extracting information in the forests of Vilna.

The autumn of liberation gave way to a winter of interrogation. Avram became captive to the indifferent world of the inquisitor. His fists were clenched. His jaw set tight. He did his job. It was a job that had to be done. He cross-examined, exposed fabrications, forced confessions.

As for those whom he interrogated? Sometimes Avram registered their terror. Their cries for mercy. In a war waged among civilians there were many losers. Such as the young Lithuanian woman who kept a diary which indicated she had slept with SS officers.

She seemed small and pathetic. She trembled with fear. She wore cheap lipstick. Her powdered cheeks could not hide her ageing skin. Her barely audible replies trailed off as she lowered her eyes and gnawed her polished nails.

So this is what it has come to, thought Avram. The front was moving westwards. The Red Army was advancing in triumph, while he was condemned to crawl in the shadows and extract confessions from those who had slept with the enemy.

Avram's unit returned to Vilna where he continued his intelligence work. One by one they found each other, pre-war comrades, childhood friends who had survived. They would meet in the evenings to play cards and exchange their extraordinary tales.

Avram was a valued member of this band. As an intelligence officer he had access to stocks of food: rolls of salami, herring, cheese; and flagons of vodka, their 'medicine'. His scruples had softened. He agreed to accumulate the precious supplies and deliver them to his comrades.

Avram lay on his dormitory bed. Beside him lay a bag packed with food and drink. In the evening he was to meet his friends. It was a Sunday afternoon in the winter of 1944, and he was engrossed in *The Stormy Life of Lazik Roitschwantz*, a novel written by the Soviet writer Ilya Ehrenburg. He would remember the exact page, the precise passage, and little else, when he next awoke. The hero of the novel was escaping from Russia to Paris. It would be the last thing Avram would remember for many weeks to come.

Avram awoke six weeks later in a military hospital. The face of a woman entered into his field of vision. As the lens widened he saw her sitting beside the bed. She was wearing a white coat. Behind her floated orderlies and nurses, a world of white upon white.

She began to question him. Gently. Avram had lost his memory, except for four vital facts, which he clung to with tenacity. He could recite them over and again.

Fact one: he was a partisan.

Fact two: he was a Yid.

Fact three: he was a Vilner.

Fact four: his mother and sister had been murdered by the Nazis.

That was all. And for the time being, it was enough, except for the food that was placed beside his bed, as if in reward for his startling performance.

Avram fell upon the food like a famished beast. The questioning resumed; and the four facts persisted. Avram recited them in a monotone: I am a partisan. I am a Yid. I am a Vilner. And my mother and sister were murdered.

The psychiatrist changed tack. She held up a chart with the letters of the Russian alphabet. Avram identified them with ease. She handed him a book. He placed his cheeks against the paper. He smelt the pages. Ran his fingers over the text. He saw the letters come into focus, the words form; he gathered in the sentences.

Avram had always worshipped books. They were his father's most valued possessions. It was a passion he had transmitted to his son. Their Vilna apartment had been crowded with books. They tumbled off the living-room shelves, lay at random upon the kitchen table, clung to every available space.

Avram can still recall the book the doctor gave him. It was an account of the Spanish Civil War; and it was a wise choice. Not too intimate a subject as to overwhelm, but close enough to his deepest interests to excite his imagination, his love of history and ideas. As he read it, memory, history's indispensable but fragile partner, began to return. Avram lapsed in and out of sleep. He floated between the printed page and his fractured dreams.

Through his barely opened eyes he glimpsed the psychiatrist. She stood by the bed with a colleague. 'This is an interesting case,' Avram heard her whisper. 'A boy from Vilna. They found him in the streets. Lying unconscious, in a pool of blood. He had a deep gash on his forehead. He was without documents, without arms. All he had as identification was his Red Army coat. He lay in a coma for six weeks from which he has just emerged. He is still suffering from amnesia.'

'Is your name Avramel?' the visiting doctor asked.

'Yes,' the patient replied. And was startled into a sudden remembrance of himself. Of a child called Avramel. Avramele. Names first heard in the cradle, within a trusting world.

'Is your family name Zeleznikow?'

'Yes.'

'And you had a sister called Basia?'

'Yes.'

'And a father called Yankel?'

'Yes.'

'And a mother called Etta?'

'Yes.'

'And you lived in an apartment at Benedictinski 4?'

'Yes.'

'I knew them all. My name is Dr Baranowski. I sometimes visited your house. Your father was a friend of mine. I knew you when you were a child.'

Etta. Yankel. Basia. Avramel. A family called Zeleznikow. An apartment at Benedictinski 4. The doctor had touched on the intimate core. A samovar bubbled, centre table. Shadows played upon the walls. Yankel, Etta and their guests sipped brandy and tea. They mapped out missions and talked of ambitious schemes. Avramel lay in bed, in the adjoining room, and was lulled to sleep by the babble of voices. They argued late into the night, enveloped by warmth and light.

Avram glimpsed familiar faces, shimmering white. And beyond them, he saw the white coat of the doctor who stood above him. She was smiling. At Avram, Avramel, Avramele. A boy with a name, an address, a past. A boy with a father and a cradle and a mother singing: Ai-le-lu-le. Ai-le-lu-le. Sleep my child in peace. Fortunate is he who has a loved one. Ai-le-lu-le-lu. Blessed is he who has a loved one. Ai-le-lu-le-lu...

Avram was discharged from hospital weeks later. He reported back to intelligence headquarters. He asked for his delayed wages and was told that, in his absence, the cashier had taken his three months of pay. She was involved in an affair with a Red Army officer, and had become pregnant. She needed an abortion. She was desperate for the money.

'Forget it,' advised Avram's commanding officer. 'If I report her, she will be sent to Siberia, and you will not regain your pay anyhow. She will repay you with sexual favours, if you wish. Screw her and forget it. We still want to keep you. You have a talent for intelligence work. You are an experienced interrogator.

'We will send you to the Crimea for a rest. And from there you will be sent to a special school in Moscow. We will put your skills to good use.'

'It sounded okay to me,' Avram tells me. 'I signed the paper. I didn't care. Nothing mattered to me. It did not seem important. Two days later I was approached by a Red Army captain. He was a member of my intelligence unit.

'"Are you a Yid?" he asked.

'"Yes."

'"I must tell you something in confidence. You must promise to keep it to yourself. Do you know what papers you have signed? Do you know what sort of school they are sending you to?"

'"I have no idea."

'"It is a centre for the study of espionage, a school that trains spies. Once you enter it, they will never let you go. You will be trapped for life. If you want to get out while there is still time, I can help you. This is your only chance. When you attend your medical examination ask to be seen by Dr T. He will know what to do."

'"And who are you? Why do you want to help me?"

'"I am a disciple of the Lubavicher rebbe. He has told me, I can do whatever I like. Eat pork. Drink vodka. Sleep around. Forsake my prayers. As long as I save Jewish lives."

'The next morning I went to the medical centre. Dr T gave me a certificate that stated I had epilepsy, due to my recent injuries. I would no longer be reliable as an interrogator or spy.

When I returned to my commanding officer he took one look at my certificate and ordered me out. "I never want to see you again," he said. "But do not reveal you have ever been here. Do not breathe a word of what you have been involved in."

'I left the barracks that had been my home for many months. I wandered the streets of Vilna. Again, I was alone; and free of expectations, of all care. An hour or so later I ran into Nina Gerstein. I had known her all my life. Her family lived in the floor above us at Benedictinski 4. I did not know she had survived.'

'She lives in Mexico now. I have met her many times,' says Masha, who has rejoined us. Her voice sounds disembodied, as if drifting from afar.

'You see, I have got a witness. Now you know what I have been telling you is completely true,' says Avram with an ironic smile. 'Nina told me she had spent the war years in Vilna, hidden in a house beyond the ghetto walls. She was being repatriated to Poland in the next few days. This was my big chance. She urged me to leave with her. She was fifteen years older than I. By law, survivors under twenty-one years of age could be adopted by Polish citizens, as long as we were not employed in important work.'

'You see, Martin, it was fated. *Beshert,*' says Masha.

'I received my documents from the city council,' continues Avram. 'I had lost my intelligence job just in time. My birth certificate proved I was still under twenty-one, by just two months. Days later, as we crossed from Soviet-occupied

Lithuania into Poland, I heard the news that Hitler had suicided. I arrived in Lodz on May Day, 1945. And fourteen months later I met Masha. Yes. You could say it was *beshert*.'

'He was wild when I met him,' says Masha. 'He would suddenly explode. Without warning. At the slightest provocation.'

'I am still wild.'

'He is joking. But in those days, when I first met him I was wary. I was unsure; but he kept me with his stories. When I heard them, I understood.'

'I look back at that time,' says Avram, 'and I see a man out of control. But I had to find a way out. I needed someone who would listen.'

'His stories were unbelievable,' says Masha.

'A thousand and one nights it would take to tell them all,' adds Avram.

'I can still listen to them,' says Masha, 'and over the years I have noticed changes. He sees things differently with each telling. He is softening. But when I met him he was a man full of mistrust. I could see it in his eyes. If not for the stories I would have run. I was young. I had plans. I was not burdened by so much darkness.'

'I fell in love with her the moment I saw her; and heard her name. She had a twisted ankle, and walked with a limp. And she was called Masha. I could not believe it. I had known another Masha. We had met in 1938, when I was fourteen years old. Vilna was my whole life, and I was in love with Masha. She was my first love. And she vanished into the same darkness that consumed all my loved ones. Now I was looking at a beautiful woman called Masha. I knew that I could not afford to let her go. I knew instantly that I would pursue her to ends of the earth.'

'I did not take to him at first,' says Masha. 'I was suspicious. I sensed something else; and it frightened me. And, in years to come, what I sensed was to prove true.'

'Martin, I have never told Masha this. When I fell in love with the first Masha, I would lie in bed on winter nights and write her name on the frosted windowpane. I always coupled her name with two other words, all beginning with M. *Masha. Mamme. Makht.* Masha. Mother. Strength.'

'It does not surprise me,' says Masha. 'In later years I would have to mother him. I could feel it even then, that he needed a lot of care. But he was very determined. He pursued me. The next time we met, after our first encounter at the Bund camp, was when he stopped over in Katowice. I had not yet moved to Lodz. He was on party business, and he invited me to the hotel. So I went. I was naive. Of course, he wanted to take me, immediately.'

'I only wanted to give her a kiss,' says Avram, laughing. 'Instead, she slapped me. It was a full-blooded *patsch,* in the face; and it was wonderful to feel it. In the forests I had lost all desire for sex. Like everything else, it seemed brutal. There were partisans who fell upon each other like animals. Sometimes we had to defend our women from partisans who lusted over them.

There were some who did pair off, who found comfort in each other's arms. But most of us had lost our desire. There is a Russian saying. It is a curse. *Zhit budiesh no yebat nye zekhotches*. May you live, but lose the will to screw. And I remained cursed until, with one glance, at the first sight of Masha, in the summer of 1946, my desire returned with full force.'

'He did not let go. He pursued me. Whenever he saw me with other men, he was jealous; but he did not give up. After I moved to Lodz we would go for long walks to the theatre, the cinema and city parks; and he was always telling me stories. In a way he was cunning. He could see how beguiled I was. And he was a legend, a partisan, a fiery speaker at Bund rallies. A survivor of Vilna, the famous cradle of Yiddish life. Also, I must admit, he was a good-looking boy.'

'What can I say? When I met Masha, I knew I could not lose her. I had lost too much.'

'It was not so simple for me. There was a long way to go before I fell in love with him. Even when we did finally become lovers, I still saw the signs, the moments of rage. Martin, it is a long story. Do you have time for all this?'

'I met Masha. She listened. She took me back to my first love. Perhaps, after all, it was *beshert*.'

Beshert. It is a word impossible to translate. An Hebraic word, with many layers of meaning. A word which invokes treks across biblical landscapes. An expression which contains the traces of chance encounters that change lives, and epic voyages towards the light. A word which hints at miracles. Or, perhaps, just mere coincidences. A term which twists its way back to Masha and Avram, to the first intimations of love.

VIII

In Acland Street, St Kilda, there stands a cafe called Scheherazade. Yes, dear reader, the question still remains: why did Avram and Masha choose that name? We have sat through long evenings, and greeted many dawns. We have met so many times, on Sunday mornings and week-day afternoons. We have seen the turning of the seasons, the passage of three full years. *Nu*?

'It is simple,' says Avram.

'Not so simple,' claims Masha. 'First we should tell Martin how we left Poland. Actually, I did not want to leave Poland. I was happy in Lodz. I was studying to be a doctor. Instead I became a refugee all over again. A nobody.'

'For a time I felt the same,' says Avram. 'I thought we could rebuild our lives in Poland. But after the Kielce pogrom I was not so sure. I was sent there, in July 1946, as a member of a Bund delegation, to investigate. Out of a pre-war population of forty-five thousand, two hundred Jews had returned to Kielce after the war, from the Soviet Union, from the camps and places of hiding.

'The police confiscated the pistols of the returnees the day before the pogrom. They had no means to defend themselves. Forty-two Jews were murdered in the assault. Our delegation was denied entry to the city, but I saw some of the injured when we returned to Lodz.

'Their wounds were terrible. Some even had stiletto marks imprinted on their faces. They were attacked by a mob, by men clutching knives, and women who used their pointed heels as weapons. They battered their victims in a frenzy. When I looked at the wounded my old suspicions returned; and my bitterness, my rage.

'Yet even then I wanted to stay. Not all Poles were anti-Semites. There were Poles who had saved Jewish lives. There were Poles who had been our comrades in the forest, or worked with us in the partisan underground. If I have learnt nothing else, it is this. No one has a monopoly over hatred. No one has a monopoly over suffering.

'The final blow came in 1948 when the Communist Party absorbed the Polish socialists. We understood what this meant. Once the Bolsheviks came to power there would be no compromise. The Bund would become a prime target. We had no alternative but to escape.'

'I was anxious to finish my studies,' says Masha. 'I had reached the fourth year. But I also had no choice. As a Bund leader in Katowice my father was in danger of being arrested. He told me if I did not join him in leaving Poland, the whole family would have to stay. I would have their lives on my conscience.'

'We were under surveillance,' says Avram. 'For months we had been smuggling out our comrades and friends. Some stole out via the port of Danzig, over the Baltic Sea to Sweden; others fled via the Tatra mountains to Czechoslovakia. We had contacts in the Polish border police, a network of smugglers and supplies.'

'I remember the day of our decision well: 25 May 1948, Avram's birthday. We were with a group of Bund comrades in an apartment in Lodz. They were all planning their escape.'

'You see, Martin, there were two ways to leave Poland,' says Avram. 'Those of us who had been very active in the Bund decided to steal across the borders. But Masha's father tried the legal option. He wanted his family to remain intact. He had applied for, and received, official exit visas, a year earlier. He decided to leave openly.'

'On that day, Avram's birthday, when he told me he was going to escape, we agreed to meet in Paris,' says Masha, pursuing another tack. 'It was then that there came to us the idea that we would celebrate our reunion in Scheherazade, as did the lovers in Remarque's novel. We would go to the nightclub and drink Calvados, the apple brandy that the lovers drank. It pleased us to think we were involved in a romance. It pleased us to think we were like characters in a novel. It lightened our burden. Besides, it was not certain that we would ever see each other again.'

Their hopes turned towards Paris. They fantasised a way out beyond their landlocked lives. At the centre of their imaginary map stood a beacon called the Arc de Triomphe. Radiating from the arch, like tracks of tinsel, sprawled the boulevards of a new dream. In their mind's eye they beheld dimly lit bridges rising from the River Seine. They saw themselves strolling over cobbled streets lit by lamps glowing like replica moons, or gliding in a carriage through the Bois de Bologne, the melodious clip-clop of hooves marking time within the shadows. They pictured the elegant decay of the Hotel International, its foyers reeking with stale carpets, its rooms layered with dust; and if its rooms proved to be too stifling, they could make their way to Scheherazade, a lover's retreat.

After all, despite all they had endured, Masha was twenty-one and Avram twenty-four, when they decided to leave Poland.

Avram left in mid-September 1948, when the first cold winds began to blow. The countryside lay resplendent under a veil of golds. Mid-morning frost rose from the earth. The land was spent, the harvest all but over; ochre haystacks and cow dung lay scattered over fallow fields.

There were six in the group: four men and two women. Comrades, toughened through years of struggle, buoyed by each other's company, and young enough to feel the thrill of intrigue. They were veterans, masters of stealth in times of danger. Each one had seen death many times over, felt its presence, inhaled its stench.

They journeyed by train south, from Lodz to Katowice. They squeezed into a taxi and drove deep into the Tatra mountains. They got out several kilometres from the Czech border, and moved on by foot, guided by a professional smuggler. They descended through a forest to a frontier stream, hid until evening, and waded across the border at night.

Many years later, what they would recall about this moment was not the fear, but their amused irritation as Avram chewed a bar of chocolate. The crackle of silver foil grated on their ears. It took a supreme effort to restrain themselves from breaking out into fits of laughter.

They crept over a strip of no man's land, and continued on, by foot, through the night, towards the Czech city of Bratislava. They approached its outskirts at dawn, joined Czechoslovaks on the way to work, and merged with the moving crowds. They made their way to the central station, and boarded a train to Prague.

They allowed themselves time to visit Prague's renowned synagogue, and the ancient cemetery that had miraculously survived the war intact, but moved on before the day was over. Now that they had set their sights on the west, they did not want to look back.

They entrained for Germany. They crossed over the Czech–German border with ease. For the first time they were not questioned. Their safe passage had been prearranged. They stepped off the train in Munich. Avram could not abide the thought of remaining there for even a day. Munich was the heartland of the former Reich. Dachau concentration camp was nearby; and just 160 kilometres to the north, stood the bombed city of Nuremberg.

A mere decade earlier the Nazi Party had marched over its cobbled streets. They held aloft banners of the eagle as predator. They had gathered, in their tens of thousands, on the outskirts, in the assembly grounds, on fields and runways where the Nuremberg rallies took place.

Whenever Avram saw men in uniform, whether railway bureaucrats or security guards, the passion for revenge shook his whole being. The final glimpse of his mother returned to goad him on. 'Take care of yourself in the forest,' she told him. And then she disappeared, amidst the barking of dogs, the screams of the wounded, arm-in-arm with her daughter, Basia, clinging to baby Nehamiah, clasping the hand of little Shmulek.

Avram moved on in haste. Now that the decision had been made, he did not want to endure a moment's delay. And there was something else: his longing for Masha, a girl with blue-green eyes. Only now that they were separated did he realise how intense this longing was.

He left the group and travelled on alone, west from Munich to Stuttgart, where he met up with a former comrade. Together they journeyed to the French border, guided by a smuggler. They hid in a cemetery until nightfall. The smuggler directed them to a church that stood against the border. They scaled a brick wall and Germany was behind them.

They made their way to the nearest station, boarded the final night train, avoided the gaze of conductors, and remained curled up on their seats, their faces concealed by the dark. Their imagined freedom was within their grasp. Yet the hours dragged by.

They finally drifted into an uneasy sleep. They journeyed through one last night; and awoke to a sprawl of Parisian suburbs, radiant in the morning light. It was 23 September 1948: Avram would always remember the exact date.

The Frydmans left Poland in the first week of October, almost a month after Avram. They left together: Masha, her father Joseph, her mother Yohevet, her sister Sala, the entire family, except for her younger brother, Lonka, who had preceded them to Paris. They left with official exit visas, and four hundred books packed tightly in wooden crates.

At the Polish–German border, officers entered their carriage. They examined their passports, stared at their photos. Masha recalls her fear, her heart pounding, her helplessness before these uniformed men. As the Polish border police searched their bags, the Frydmans adopted the pose they knew so well; they shrank back in their seats, as if trying to become invisible. One suspicious glance, one word out of place, would have betrayed their cause.

Nevertheless, Joseph was arrested, and led away. No explanations were given. The three women were left stranded. They returned to Katowice.

For three weeks they made inquiries, knocked on doors, prowled the corridors, waited for hours in police stations and government offices, until they finally traced their father to the city jail. And their fear returned; an ancient fear, compounded by so many false exits. Years later, in Melbourne, this fear would surge up whenever Masha saw policemen in uniform. She would cross the street to avoid their gaze, and she would hurry away, as if to suppress the memory of the moment when, yet again, her dash for freedom was derailed.

In Paris, Avram counted the days. He felt Masha's absence as a burning ache. As the time for her scheduled arrival drew closer, his anxiety increased. He made his way to the Gare de Lyon with a fearful heart. As the train he believed she would be on drew into the station, he scanned each carriage, each exit in vain. All that arrived were the four hundred books.

When Avram learnt what had happened to the Frydmans, he decided to return to Poland. It was simple: he could not live without Masha. But it was a dangerous mission. He needed a false passport and disguise. He waited nervously for the passport to arrive. He wandered the streets of Paris driven by a feeling of dread. The city had lost its imagined appeal. The Arc de Triomphe appeared cold, a hollow colossus, sagging with defeat. The Eiffel Tower was a weight of naked girders streaking into leaden skies. The City of Lights was an inaccessible vision. Its cafes mocked him with their promise of companionship. Sounds of laughter grated upon his ears.

Avram became acutely aware of the other city, within the shadows. He observed the weary-eyed revellers, searching like robots for half-remembered thrills. He saw those who wandered alone, kindred spirits in search of lost love. His gaze was drawn to the flights of steps, which descended to the lower embankments and netherworlds.

He could imagine them all too well, the sewers that threaded beneath the city's elegant streets. After all, they threaded through his dreams; a recurring nightmare of a man forever crawling through shit, through the incessant dripping of urine and sweat, a man tunnelling through the city's intestines for a way out. The tunnels spiralled into dead ends. He did not know where they led. Or under which city he was burrowing. Was it Vilna or Paris? Or was it a nameless city where informers begged for mercy with the terror of death in their eyes, a city where those who made love at dawn were hanged before the day was out?

Yet even these nightmares were preferable to the dreams of loved ones he had lost. They appeared before him in a revolving procession. Basia. Yankel. Shmulek. Nehamiah. And Etta, with a scarf held tight in her hands. 'Take care of yourself in the forest,' she whispered. And in her place, like an apparition, appeared the face of a girl with blue-green eyes; her name was etched in the frost; and Avram was back in a room in Vilna.

He could hear the sounds of the mahogany piano drifting in from an adjoining room. A woman was playing; the keys flashed black and white like rotting teeth. Again he was disoriented. Was it his sister Basia playing the piano, or the girl with the blue-green eyes?

More faces appeared, at once distinct and vague; they vanished into the darkness from which they had emerged and in their place he observed faces of cruelty and stone, hovering over makeshift tables, barking orders, laughing.

Avram would will himself to awake; and he awoke alone, in the hotel room where he had imagined spending his first nights of consummated love. He glanced out of the window at a skyline of gables, spires and domes; a familiar skyline, his childhood Vilna writ large. He heard the hissing of the heating pipes, a cough in an adjoining room. He listened to the snarling of cats at war in a back lane.

Avram left his room and prowled corridors that smelt of stale cabbage and dust. Through a door, left momentarily ajar, he glimpsed a Russian emigre seated in front of an icon of his patron saint. The icon stood on an improvised altar, behind a solitary candle in which there flickered an ancient dream of return.

In a nearby room sat a circle of exiles, in flight from Franco's Spain. They were scanning newspapers from which they raised their heads to argue with each other. Or was it merely a futile attempt to pass time?

In the room opposite sat a grey-bearded Algerian, on the edge of his bed, his gaze fixed upon the wall. Who was he waiting for? How long had he been adrift? How long had he been spitting blood with each uncontrollable cough? Most likely he had made his way from the outposts of a dying empire to the City of Lights, only to find the doors locked; only to discover he was, after all, an outsider, an interloper from foreign shores.

In every room suitcases lay in corners, under beds, against walls. Some rooms had collapsible spirit-cookers, and a few odd utensils, a frying pan, a knife, a fork, or perhaps an all-purpose spoon.

The hotel was a universe of fading wallpaper and rickety chairs; of sagging mattresses in bare-boned rooms lit by a single bulb. There were times when every inmate, from the night porter to the last guest, seemed to be aflame with that exhausted longing so characteristic of the displaced.

As for Avram, his longing had been reduced to just one face. He ran his hands over his growing beard. He inquired daily after his fake passport. He spent his days at the Bund locale, where his comrades urged him to be patient. But at night he continued to steal through the streets, his mind ablaze with one thought. He barely registered the passing avenues, the neighbourhood squares, the dark waters of the River Seine. He was blind to the world about him. As he wandered, all he could see was the face of the girl with the blue-green eyes. With each echoing step, his longing mounted; and, with each passing night, the city seemed to mock him even more.

The three women made their way to the Katowice jail. The authorities refused them permission to visit Joseph. Masha travelled to Warsaw to plead on his behalf. After much persuasion and bribes, the Frydmans were allowed into Joseph's cell.

'Do not wait for me,' he urged. 'Leave for Paris. I am sure I will be released. But do not wait. It is time to get out.'

It was both a plea and a command.

Masha, Sala and Yohevet resumed their journey west. It was as if they had never ceased travelling. They were back on the same rails that had held so much promise just seven weeks before. And they feared the worst. They travelled not knowing whether they would see Joseph again.

They arrived in Paris in mid-December. The streets were hidden under a pall of snow. The city was masked by a white silence. Avram was at the station to greet them; his fake papers were yet to arrive. But his reunion with Masha was now tainted by Joseph's absence. The couple greeted each other without a sense of triumph. They had been stripped of any desire to celebrate. They could not rest until Joseph was free. They spent their days exploring every possible option for his release.

Two months later, in mid-February 1949, Avram and Masha answered a knocking at their hotel door, and saw Joseph standing in front of them, suitcase in hand. He appeared like a phantom returned from the dead. His clothes were frayed, his eyes gaunt. He was unshaven. He looked exhausted. But he had survived.

Several weeks later, in the first month of spring, 1949, Masha and Avram set out for their rendezvous at Scheherazade.

They went to the nightclub by taxi. They stepped out at the Place Pigalle. Broad boulevards radiated a confusion of options. They circled the neighbourhood. They walked through a warren of streets littered with cafes and music halls.

Waiters beckoned passers-by into their bars. The sounds of an accordion drifted through an open door. Semi-naked women of the night scouted for clients, their powdered faces lit by the glare of neon signs. Avram and Masha glanced up at lamps blinking like mysterious beacons on the Montmartre heights. And, just as they were about to give up, they found it, below a flight of stairs, near the corner where they had first stepped out.

An attendant dressed in a Cossack uniform greeted them at the door. Masha and Avram walked through the pages of their beloved novel. They walked across a dance floor encircled by tables. Each table stood in a separate niche. Avram asked for a bottle of Calvados. First you must buy a bottle of champagne, the waiter explained, for a cover charge of eight thousand francs.

They emptied their pockets. They could barely pay the required sum. They sat for hours by one glass of champagne; they did not eat. Serenading violinists strolled by the tables. Avram and Masha sat in the spotlighted darkness, as a singer crooned Russian folk songs, 'Katusha' and 'Dark Eyes'. It was a nostalgic charade which nonetheless revived memories of Red Army soldiers singing in the afternoon mists, of snow-bound steppes, and forests of conifers and birch.

They sat in the semi-darkness at a glass-topped table. Avram inhaled the scent of perfume. He closed his eyes and touched the warm hands of the girl with the blue-green eyes; he felt the tightness in his fingers give way.

Avram and Masha made their way to the dance floor. They

danced to the music of a Gypsy orchestra. How long was it since Avram had yielded so easily to touch? How could he have known that this was what he had craved for in his years of exile and flight?

It would take years for Avram's anger to soften; but now he was dancing in Scheherazade, with its painted scenes of St Petersburg palaces, and cathedrals with onion-shaped domes. They danced in the shadows of lost childhoods, when the frost flowed with each breath. They danced to the memories of horse-drawn sledges, gliding over streets gilded with ice.

Masha drew close. Avram seemed to radiate the faint scent of resinous forests, the traces of his perilous journeys. As she danced Masha recalled her own journeys, a girl struggling, waist-deep, through a landscape of snow. A lone figure was stealing out into the Siberian night, beneath a sky vaulting with unknown galaxies and indifferent stars. Then she was back in Paris, in Scheherazade, warmed by her partner's touch; and she was moving across the dance floor, to the minor keys of a Gypsy violin.

Masha observed, as if for the first time, how young her partner was. His black hair was ample and thick, combed back in waves. She felt his strength; the body toughened by the hard earth on which it had slept, and the caches of arms it had hauled on forest raids.

Avram and Masha savoured the passing hours. They danced to the last strains of the violins, sipped their last drop of champagne, ascended the stairs, and embarked on the long stroll home.

They walked the avenues of the Pigalle past bistros where groups of men huddled over games of baccarat. They moved beneath street lamps that cast their lights on the branches of sycamore trees. Even at this hour, at least one light remained burning in each apartment building; a reminder that there was always life.

Avram took Masha's hand. He felt light. Unburdened. He was surging; in this moment he did not fear the sound of footsteps, nor did he imagine the whispers of stalkers moving in his wake. He marvelled at the events of this night. Scheherazade had not betrayed him. It was the first dream that had not betrayed him for many years.

Masha too felt light. It had been so long since she had first taken flight, since she had crossed the borders to the east, accompanied by the sounds of Red Army soldiers singing 'Katusha' on a winter breeze. Years later, she was still on the move, gliding along the Champs Elysees to the arch of forgotten triumphs.

Masha and Avram stopped by the tomb of the unknown soldier, with its eternal blue flame. They glanced at the single flower, a quiver of memory that someone had placed upon the grave. They strolled on aimlessly and descended to the lower embankments of the Seine. A barge drifted past lit by a solitary lamp. In the shadows lovers pressed close to each other, as if this night was to be their last.

And still they walked, Masha and Avram, hand in hand, through mazes of alleys and boulevards, in and out of silent courtyards, through visible layers of time. There were moments when Avram thought he was hallucinating. The sight of an arch, of serpentine streets and cathedral spires, and he was back in Vilna, retracing the footsteps of a child. Paris was so like Vilna, even down to the plane trees and chestnuts that had lined the avenues of his childhood strolls.

It was touch that brought him back, the gentle pressure of a hand. He glanced at Masha and, in the stillness of the pre-dawn, he saw the fierce determination with which she walked. She moved with the same sense of purpose she applied to all aspects of her life. And she saw, moving beside her, a troubled man; and again she knew it would be difficult. She had always known this, but for now they were lovers moving side by side, accompanied by the echo of their footsteps, by the harmony of their breath.

The dark gave way to the first light of a cool dawn. Avram and Masha entered the narrow streets of the Algerian quarter. Cleaners swept the gutters. Shopkeepers raised their steel-ribbed shutters. Carts trundled through cobbled lanes. Workers bent over bowls of coffee in run-down cafes. A Buick glided by, with a smaller Renault in its wake. Workers hurried to the Metro and descended its stone steps like miners disappearing into the earth.

Avram and Masha made their way to the entrance of their cheap lodgings. They climbed the wooden stairs to their single room. All the long years were now pared back to this room which lay beyond the cruel gaze of dictators. Here life could resume the unhurried rhythms of love, free from terror.

Avram lay in the afterglow of love. He glanced about the room, noted the chair draped by a dress, by a slip and discarded stockings, illuminated by the ascending light of day. Beside him lay Masha, asleep. He moved closer, and regained her softness, her warmth.

He got up and closed the wooden shutters, returned to the bed, ran his hand over her body again. The room was full of her presence. Yes, love was a physical presence, full-blooded, a definable force.

He had known variations of this presence once before. At Benedictinski 4. As he lay beneath an eiderdown, knowing that nearby hovered his protectors, his father who wove grand visions, and his mother who would enter his room, to tend to his illnesses, to make sure he was warm. This was Etta's only thought when she saw Avram for the final time. She wrapped him in her scarf, in her warmth. Then she was gone.

Avram rested his hand upon Masha's breast, as if to reassure himself she was not an illusion. He watched the rise and fall of her breath. He glimpsed the ascending sun through the slats of the shutters.

Their rendezvous was over, but their journey had not ended. They were, after all, 'displaced persons', still on the move. Before them lay many more months of waiting, the humiliation of meals in soup kitchens, the twice-weekly visits to the police, the eternal round of visa stamps, queues and interrogations, the nerve-sapping search for a home.

Before them lay many more walks through the City of

Lights. They roamed Paris like children let loose at a fun fair. 'Walking is cheap. Walking does not cost,' they reasoned. 'Walking is a way to pass time while our lives are still on hold.'

They came to know neighbourhood courtyards with children at play. They strolled over the Pont Neuf to the left bank, and sat in its cafes. For the price of a glass of soda they could sit for an entire evening at marble-topped tables, with their heads buried in *Le Monde* or *Paris Soir,* and pretend they belonged there.

Theirs was still a counterfeit life; and there were times when Paris seemed closed to them, leaving them stranded at its padlocked gates. Yet still they walked, even if it was on uncertain ground, from the left bank back to the right; they paused upon the city's bridges from which they gazed upon the Notre Dame, the cathedral of Our Lady. It reared in the night sky like a citadel, concealing stone pillars and cold vaults.

After nights of love-making the city would regain its radiance. It was in the small details that a world they had almost forgotten reappeared: leaves regained their veins; the waters of the Seine were a pageant of lustrous greens; a sudden ray of sun became a shaft of gold; the breeze a refreshing spirit; a cloud-ridden sky an ocean of silver-greys.

The rendezvous was over, but before them lay many more nights in that single room; spring nights scented with jasmine and budding blooms; summer nights laden with sultry skies, autumn nights imminent with storms; winter nights echoing with falling snow; full moon nights when tiled roofs shone and the city was cast in an unearthly glow; countless nights on which recurring stories gave way to silent dawns.

Yes, the rendezvous was over, and there were nights when other faces intruded. Faces contorted with cruelty. Unwanted faces that Avram could not tame. They dragged him back into the darkness, to the smell of terror, to the ache of his all-too-recent wounds. He wanted to interrogate them. He wanted to scream out the eternal why. And he would awake to his hardened breath; and the redeeming softness of Masha's presence. He would gaze at her, reach over and touch her; touch her hair, her face, her bare arms.

Yes, the rendezvous was over, and before them lay many nights when Avram recoiled from love. Nights when he retreated to the forests, to the memories he had concealed, to tales of partisans who fell upon their foes like enraged animals. They pointed their guns at cowering families, at the boy standing in front of his father, begging them to spare his life. At the mother, standing in front of her daughter, to shield her from their desire to rape; while watching them was a nineteen-year-old boy called Avram.

And only now, after so many nights in the back room of Scheherazade, do I see the first glitter of Masha's tears. Only now, after so many hours of self-control, does Masha speak of the moments when she had come across him, unexpectedly, or had approached him from behind, and laid a gentle hand upon his shoulder; and he had turned, with his arms raised, shaking with suspicion, ready to defend himself, back in the forests, alert like a wild animal to the stalking of a hunter; and he would turn on her as if she were a stranger.

Avram gently rocks at the remembrance. He stretches out a gentle hand to Masha. Touches her on the shoulder. And whispers, yes, she had to withstand so much confusion, so much rage.

We are drawn together, the three of us, in a circle of subdued light, and in that light, Avram and Masha seem transparent, fully revealed. Avram's hand is resting, softly, upon Masha's shoulder; and he is whispering 'Yes, she had to endure so much. But, tell me, how could anyone come out of that *gehennim* whole or sane?'

Then we are back in Paris, where Avram's tales were absorbed in a lover's arms. Where the first child was conceived, born and bathed. Where love was first regained.

No. Scheherazade had not betrayed them. The Gypsy orchestra still awaited them. For the price of a bottle of champagne they could remain in the half-light, in the recesses, or glide to the strains of a violin; to the melodies of those who live on the fringes, who know both brutality and romance, who know that only in love can there be redemption, a permanent home.

Before them lay an ocean, and another voyage to an uncertain life, to a new world, and a new city, perched on its southern extremes; a city with a street crowded with cafes and restaurants based upon old-world dreams. And years later, when they embarked upon their audacious venture, what option did they have but to call it Scheherazade?

IX

Sanctuary is the word that comes to mind. It can be sensed at the entrance to Melbourne's Port Phillip Bay: a narrow opening, a three-kilometre stretch of water, between two peninsulas that sweep towards each other like hands reaching out to complete an embrace.

A line of foam marks the divide where the open ocean and bay collide. Incoming waves break before the outgoing tide. They call it the Rip, this gauntlet that ships must run to gain the protection of the bay. Over the years many have faltered at the threshold, in clashing tides and winds, in contending currents and submarine drifts.

I try to imagine it, as it may have seemed to those who arrived here in search of new lives. Perhaps this is how they saw it: the bay opening up in an ample embrace, a glimpse of gnarled she-oaks and scrub, of sea grasses clasping at low-slung dunes, the flight of a gold-hooded gannet, wings extended, scanning the waters for its prey.

A place of refuge. An ample embrace. A seabird's graceful glide. These are the images that come to mind. This is how I like to imagine the moment of arrival. But would they have perceived it as such? Zalman, Yossel and Laizer? Masha and Avram?

The war was long over. They had received their papers, their hard-earned permits. Their journey was nearing its end. The wharf was approaching. The city was manifest before their eyes. And yet?

Zalman recalls his state of mind. The city was an apparition, its features obscured by bitter thoughts. He was still a young man. And a cynic. By the time he left Shanghai, in January 1949, his youthful sense of anticipation was long gone.

'It was just another city coming into view. I did not see myself as coming here to build a new life. I had no ambition. I just came. I wanted to drink, make merry and pass the time. I wanted only to live for the day. I wanted to have as many affairs as possible. I had no grand plans for a permanent home. I no longer cared what people thought. The city was just another imposition. Another joke.'

And Laizer? He recalls mere glimpses: the lighthouses upon the alternate points, one black, the other white. The wreckage of a ship glued to an outcrop of rocks. The occasional mansion overlooking a strip of deserted beach. An expanse of flatlands, broken by two shallow hills; the distant city hovering like a mirage; the wooden customs sheds surfacing upon the pier.

But for the most part he was captive to a mind filled with jousting images of the past; a mind leached by Siberian snows, bleached by Arctic winds. And a heart swamped by the feelings which had overwhelmed him when he returned to the streets of the city of his birth to find his house erased from the face of the earth. And with it his entire family. His friends. His

216

classmates. His former life. So he had left, within hours, knowing he would never return.

And Yossel? The landscape which appeared about him made little impression. It was irrelevant, a mere backdrop at the periphery of his vision. He was already at work as he entered the bay. He scoured his address books. He underlined the names of contacts, gem dealers and market stall-holders, factory foremen and speculators. His mind teemed with the same schemes that had allowed him to prosper, wherever he had gone. The city was yet another arena of opportunity to revel in, to impress upon with his cunning and charm. A place for future fortunes made, fortunes lost, wealth squandered, wealth regained.

Yossel stepped ashore with a sense of anticipation. His heart was light. He envisaged a new paradise of crowded cafes and meeting rooms, of hotel foyers and elevators, soft carpets and polished floors. He glanced about him, sniffed the air, and knew at once what was what.

And Masha? Avram?

Masha has the clearer recollection. A sense of isolation was her dominant feeling. The surrounding land seemed to reflect it: the empty beaches, the windswept dunes, the expanse of low-slung houses squatting by the coast. She felt adrift, disconnected from the vibrant cities of her past. She saw the new city as a wasteland. She had a baby to nurse. And she harboured regrets, resentment over ambitions thwarted.

Yet, in time, a sanctuary it proved to be. It is Zalman who

holds the key. We sit in Scheherazade, at the window table, from which we can observe the passers-by. 'I know now, there are moments,' says Zalman. 'There will always be moments. This was the memory that returned to me as I grew accustomed to yet another city. The space allowed it. The sense of peace fostered it.

'I resumed my walks in search of those moments of solitude and grace. And they returned. In the slight nod of a passer-by. In a bemused smile. In the sudden rearing of a breeze, or a fog lifting on a winter's morning on the way to work.

'On such mornings I would detour to a city garden. I would sit down on a park bench and observe a single leaf, covered in dew. Gradually a droplet would form. I would watch it slide on the leaf's veins. For a moment it would balance, on the edge. I would be willing it to hang on, to remain poised, fixed in time. But slowly it would slip over, and fall. And I would say, "Ah. Now I can go to work."

'This is what all my wanderings have taught me: that the moment itself is the haven, the true sanctuary. If only we could hold on to that. And savour it. Perhaps then we would not be so inclined to tear each other to pieces.'

We remain seated as darkness descends, Zalman and I. We eat our evening meal garnished with fables and tales. We imagine cities, strung across the globe, like pearls upon a silver chain. We see frayed maps etched in the foreheads of the old men who sit at neighbouring tables. Rivulets from distant continents course through their veins.

We sit until the last customer departs. We sit until the waitresses and chefs leave for home. We sit until the night manager shows us to the door.

We make our way along Acland Street. The pavement echoes beneath our feet. The air is warm, scented with a breath of summer breeze. Teenagers weave by on rollerblades. A street-walker hovers in the shadows. She takes out a compact and powders her face. A young boy plays Beethoven's one and only violin concerto, for small change which he hopes will convey him to the great concert halls of Europe. A cardboard sign proclaims it. We stop, and listen for a while.

A man carrying a duffel bag stops every few metres to conduct imaginary conversations with passers-by. 'It was a time of evil. There were seven hundred and fifty-nine men. They were surrounded by the police, by security forces. They were trapped. What chance did they have?' He recites the same lines at every stop, the same refrain every night.

We turn left into Shakespeare Grove. We stroll to the foreshore. Families are camped on the beach. Conversations bubble like froth on a breaking wave. Toddlers wade in the shallows. Lovers lie entwined on blankets. A tram floats by, a ghost rider in full flight.

We make our way to the pier. Boats sway within the marina. Some are returning from the sea, conveying the heat of a summer's day. It can be seen on the passengers' faces as they step onto their allotted jetties: the sun absorbed into their skins, their cheeks flushed by northern winds.

The inner city rises across the water in congregations of light. All we need do is extend our hands to touch the many lives that pulse within them. The streets of the new world are emptying. A mechanised sweeper moves by, absorbing the litter of a fallen day. The streets glisten with its spray.

We follow the rim of the sea. Phosphorus dances on the lips of shallow waves. We walk as silence descends upon the bay. We walk as our own voices are stilled, and are left trailing in our wake. One tale is ending, while others begin.

Storytelling is an ancient art. They stood by the fire, the first storytellers, and held their audiences entranced. Their faces glowed, half in darkness, half in light. Their voices flowed into the star-laden night. They recounted tales of battles fought, the first woman, the first man, the first moments of love and hate.

Yet, perhaps there is something beyond our endless recycling of words. The faintest traces of sunrise seep into the sky. The first rays are moving. They wipe away the stars, one by one, teardrops suspended in space. They sweep the shadows from the night-darkened sea. Blues give way to silvers, tinged with rose. A ship makes its way in the emerging light, bound for foreign ports.

The beach is strewn with seaweed and kelp. It covers the rocks, it clings to the pier, it sprawls by the bluestone wall. It lies in piles, interlaced with driftwood and bloated fish, sodden feathers and fractured shells: the detritus of the sea. The air is still, the sky mute. Spent waves lick the shore. Sailors know the moment well. The ancients knew such moments well, the calm after the storm.

We sit on the foreshore, against the retaining wall, Zalman and I, our backs turned to the streets, beyond desire, beyond reach, in the time before tales.

And, seeing that the dawn had broken, Scheherazade fell silent, as at last she was at liberty to do.

AUTHOR'S NOTE

While all dates and historical events have, wherever possible, been checked and authenticated, this is not a book about history. Rather, it is a homage to the power of storytelling, a meditation on displacement, and on the way in which the after-effects of war linger on in the minds of survivors.

Whenever I hear of another outbreak of conflict somewhere on the globe, whenever I see images of columns of refugees snaking across war-ravaged landscapes, my thoughts turn back to the tales of survivors, living in Melbourne, many of whom I have known since my childhood.

For the record: Scheherazade restaurant and cafe does exist. Founded in 1958, it still trades at the same venue, 99 Acland Street, St Kilda. There have been a number of partners over the years, but the business was principally owned and managed by Avram and Masha Zeleznikow for forty-one years. Since their retirement in 1999, the business has passed into other hands.

While *Cafe Scheherazade* is based on actual events, and upon tales that Avram and Masha and others have told me, I have reshaped and re-imagined them. Yossel, Zalman and Laizer are composite characters, whose fictional journeys are based upon tales I have heard from many survivors. The image of the old man and his songbird, on the banks of Suzhou Creek, is partly derived from a scene I observed while travelling in China in 1985.

Wolfke's restaurant, otherwise known as Velvkeh's, did exist and I have met people who spent time there in pre-war Vilna; but in this novel it is a fictional place.

I have augmented some of the tales with information gleaned

from a number of texts. In particular I wish to acknowledge the following books: *From That Place and Time: A Memoir 1938–1947*, Lucy Dawidowicz, W.W. Norton & Co., New York, 1989; *Secret War in Shanghai*, Bernard Wasserstein, Profile Books, London, 1999; *Far from Where*, Antonia Finnane, Melbourne University Press, 1999; *The Fugu Plan*, Marvin Tokayer and Mary Swartz, Paddington Press, New York, 1979. And, for inspiration, Erich Maria Remarque's *Arc de Triomphe*, first published in 1945.

The remarkable story of Chiune Sugihara has only recently been told in full. It is a complex and intriguing tale, the details of which can be found in Hillel Levine's *In Search of Sugihara*, Free Press, New York, 1996.

I was assisted in my translations of Russian songs, and of H. Leivik's poem 'On the Tracks of Siberia', by Romek and Rivke Mokotow. The translations of the Yiddish songs are mine.

I wish to thank Pinche Wiener, Sevak Kusznir, Romek Mokotow and Alex Skovron for their support and the time they put into responding to the manuscript. I have many other people to thank. Because of their wish for anonymity, and because I have woven them into the text, many of them must remain unnamed.

Michael Heyward of Text has been a marvellous editor and publisher, with a sharp eye for both the detail and the overall tenor of the book. He grasped what I hoped to achieve from the moment I contacted him.

My wife Dora, and son Alexander, have supported me in many ways. I cannot imagine writing the book without them.

As for how the stories are told, the reader has only the author to blame.